THE ESSENTIAL ART OF

Relaxation

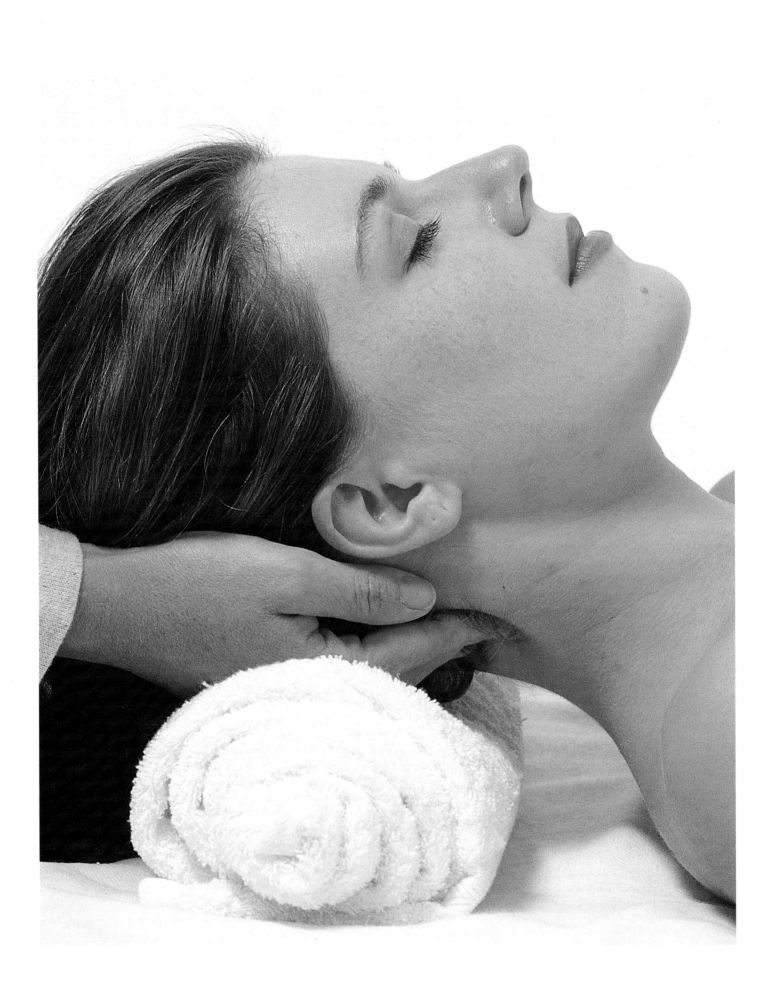

THE ESSENTIAL ART OF
Relaxation

FIONA TOY

CHANCELLOR
PRESS

Contents

Introduction

Relaxation is a state of being which seems elusive to many of us. We live life at a hectic pace with all the demands and responsibilities of work and family. Stress is not always negative and is an important and necessary part of our lives; but for most of us the balance between relaxation and stress has been lost.

Under stress our muscles contract, adrenaline is released into the bloodstream, our hearts begin to beat faster and our blood pressure increases; we breathe more quickly, our metabolism speeds up, and we sweat to keep cool. This "fight or flight" response is entirely appropriate if we are in danger, if we are about to compete or if we need to spring into action. However, our bodies react in this way, in varying degrees, to all stressful situations. If the day is a series of stressful events, providing no opportunity to release the built-up tension and energy, the body does not have time to return to a "normal" state.

When we are in a relaxed state, the rate of our heart beat and blood pressure is lower, we breathe more slowly, our muscles are less tense and our metabolism slows down.

In a *deeply* relaxed state, our brain wave patterns reduce in frequency. From the beta waves of our everyday conscious state, they move to the slower alpha waves of a relaxed state, then to the even slower theta waves of a deeply relaxed state. In this state our minds are alert yet calm and peaceful. Our metabolism, heart rate and breathing become even slower as we become more relaxed.

*Deep relaxation is a completely different state
from just socializing with friends or lying in front of the television.*

Our bodies use less oxygen and expel less carbon dioxide; our hormones return to a balanced state and blood lactate levels are reduced. Our internal organs work more effectively and, although blood pressure reduces, circulation improves with more blood reaching the extremities of the body. Our muscles become soft and loose, and we become more aware of our bodies and feelings and less aware of our surroundings. Both our minds and bodies are rested in the process of relaxing deeply.

It is important to be aware of how the different ways in which we choose to relax affect us. Not all recreational activities will leave us in a deeply relaxed state. For instance, we may enjoy watching television, seeing a film or reading a book; these activities can expand our way of seeing the world, challenging or reinforcing our beliefs; they also provide entertainment and information. They do not, however, encourage deep relaxation as television, films and books stimulate the mind — our bodies may even react to events in the stories as if we were physically involved.

Having a drink or a cup of coffee with friends provides an opportunity for self-expression, social interaction, and a sharing of common interests. This is an activity we may enjoy greatly, yet it is not a deeply relaxing experience. Meetings with friends often take place in noisy, smoky environments where we are likely to consume caffeine or alcohol; all of these factors place stress on our bodies.

The key is to find a balance between work, leisure pursuits and relaxation. Spending even a small amount of time each day in a deeply relaxed state will benefit your health and well-being. The effects of living primarily in a relaxed state or primarily in a stressed state are very pronounced.

When we are relaxed we are more likely to think clearly and be aware of what is happening around us; we are also likely to be more conscious of how we are responding to those events. High levels of energy enable us to experience unexpected events as opportunities and challenges full of possibilities. At work, we can expect to utilize time more effectively; the day will also seem to flow at a more even pace. When your energy levels are high, it is easier to

distinguish between those tasks that are important and those that are distractions masquerading as urgent.
The ability to focus makes us more efficient. When we are relaxed, we experience greater enjoyment in everything we do. Sleep is more regular, deep and peaceful, and we usually awake feeling refreshed and vital. Finding regular time for relaxation leads to an overall improvement in our health. And if we do become ill, we are more likely to recover quickly, as deep relaxation encourages the body to regain its normal self-regulation.

When we are stressed, we feel overwhelmed by the pressures of life. The list of problems seems endless. Days slip by leaving us with a sense that nothing has been accomplished, that as each day passes, we are further behind than the last. We never seem to enjoy ourselves because we are always thinking of work to be done, of the money we don't have, or the list of things that should have been done. Falling asleep may be difficult, because we are unable to switch off our ruminations about the day that has passed or the days ahead. We may wake frequently during the night or have disturbing dreams; or sometimes it seems we have only just fallen asleep when the alarm rings and another stressful day begins. Eventually this stress behavior will cause our health to deteriorate; we may become more susceptible to colds, flu and headaches.

A stressed state of being and a relaxed state of being are both self-perpetuating. To a certain extent, both are based on habit. Being stressed leads to repetitive behavior that creates stress. For example: we come home from a long day at work and the temptation is to kick off our shoes, slump into a chair and watch TV while eating a meal prepared with the least possible fuss. As a repeated pattern this behavior increases the stress in our lives. By contrast, the benefit we can feel from regularly practicing some short, simple relaxation techniques, and being aware of our diet and environment is palpable. These positive effects become in themselves the motivation to increase the time we spend in deep relaxation. Thus our stress levels are reduced even further and we soon find ourselves moving from a stress cycle to a relaxation cycle.

Stressors

The causes of stress are many and vary according to the individual. Emotional and mental causes of stress are sometimes the simplest to identify but the most difficult to remedy. Many external causes of stress may be minimized or avoided once you become aware of them. Take notice of the environment in which you live and work, and take action to reduce or eliminate those elements you feel may be creating stress in your life.

The relaxation techniques described in this book may be useful tools in changing your methods of dealing with stress in your life. The techniques are intended to be simple and practical, and suitable to be undertaken by you at home. However, if you have been stressed for a long period of time or if your health is being affected by your stress levels it would be wise to discuss your situation with a health professional.

Some common stressors are:

Emotional and mental

- Death of someone you love
- Divorce or the end of a significant relationship
- Birth of a child
- Change of job or career
- Moving house
- Deadlines and new projects
- Travelling long distances
- Any sort of major change in your routine

Environment

- Lack of fresh air and space — if you live in the city both of these factors may be difficult to overcome. Spend some time discovering your local parks or gardens.
- Noise — sharp intermittent noises can trigger a "fight or flight" response; so too can low continual noise like that emitted by air conditioning units, and the low rumble of heavy traffic or office equipment.

Diet

- Caffeine — is found in coffee, tea and cola drinks. Taken in large amounts caffeine can cause irritability, anxiety and restlessness. If you feel you are consuming too many caffeine drinks, cut back gradually; if you don't want to give them up all together, try limiting your intake to one or two drinks a day.

- Alcohol — over the years there has been conflicting evidence as to whether regular, moderate alcohol intake is detrimental to your health. More than moderate intake however is almost sure to cause problems and will place an added stress on your body. Be aware that heavy drinking can also be a symptom of stress.

Habits

- Smoking — apart from the many other medical hazards it causes, smoking reduces the amount of oxygen taken into the lungs, which immediately creates a stressful state. Contact a health professional for information on the various options available to you if you smoke and would like to give up.

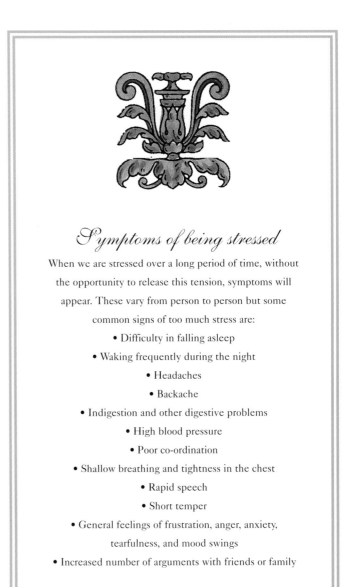

Symptoms of being stressed

When we are stressed over a long period of time, without the opportunity to release this tension, symptoms will appear. These vary from person to person but some common signs of too much stress are:

- Difficulty in falling asleep
- Waking frequently during the night
- Headaches
- Backache
- Indigestion and other digestive problems
- High blood pressure
- Poor co-ordination
- Shallow breathing and tightness in the chest
- Rapid speech
- Short temper
- General feelings of frustration, anger, anxiety, tearfulness, and mood swings
- Increased number of arguments with friends or family

Quick Tips to Relax

Rather than letting the stress cycle build, it is better to deal with minor stress quickly and effectively when it arises. There are a few simple techniques that you can put into practice whether you are at home or at work, driving or studying.

A daily routine of relaxation techniques is the most effective way to avoid becoming highly stressed. If you know that you are about to face a stressful situation there is a variety of "quick" techniques that can assist you in staying relaxed.

Take a moment to notice

When you realize you're becoming stressed, take a moment to notice what your body is doing. How is your posture? Are your shoulders relaxed? Have you been holding your breath? Which parts of your body are tense? What is causing the stress? Is the stress necessary?

In identifying which areas of your body you have tensed, you will probably find you have already relaxed them. If not, use one of the "quick tip" exercises to release the tension. If you are able to isolate the cause of the stress and you discover the stress is unnecessary, see what you can do to change the situation or your reaction to it. This way you can proceed in a relaxed state.

Smile and laugh

The age-old adage of "laughter is the best medicine" is particularly true if you're in a stressed state. A smile or a laugh can break the stress cycle and give you a different perspective on life.

The next time you feel anxious over your workload, or there's a day when everything that could go wrong has gone wrong, try to mentally take a step back and ask yourself whether being stressed and stern about it is going to improve the situation.

If you can recognize you are not going to lose time by smiling and perhaps even being able to laugh at yourself for being so serious you have taken a step towards relaxation. A good laugh releases endorphins into our bodies and improves how we feel both physically and psychologically.

Spend some time discovering what makes you smile and what makes you laugh and keep a few triggers handy, whether it's a book of cartoons, a video, or mental images you call to mind. The added bonus is that smiling and laughter are infectious, so by lightening your own day you can also lighten the day of those around you.

Sing

Singing is an effective way to release emotional tension and is especially useful if you are anxious or fearful. It helps the body relax as it increases circulation and can trigger the release of endorphins by the brain. Don't be concerned about singing in tune and sing whatever type of music you like either solo or accompanied by a recording. If you don't know the words make them up or even make nonsensical sounds. If singing feels too boisterous, start by humming a tune and work your way into a song. Use this technique wherever you like, in the car or in the shower, for example.

Five-minute meditation

You can practice this technique at home, at work, sitting in the park — anywhere you like. Sit comfortably on the floor or in a chair, making sure your back is straight, your hands lying loosely in your lap. Close your eyes. Focus on your breath moving slowly in and out of your body. Each time you breathe in, imagine yourself filling with vitality and energy. As you breathe out, imagine all the tension leaving your body. Do not become concerned if stray thoughts enter your head during this meditation, simply bring your focus back to your breath.

Shake out the tension

This effective exercise is particularly useful in a work situation. Find a private spot in which you can practice — it only takes a minute or two.

Firstly, stretch upwards inhaling deeply, then let your breath out with a "ha", flop your upper body over at the waist and let your arms hang loosely downwards. Lift each shoulder alternately to "shake out" tension in the shoulders and upper back and slowly nod your head to release tension in the neck muscles.

Stand upright again and take two or three deep breaths focusing on releasing any remaining tension. Create a mental image of staying calm and relaxed throughout the day.

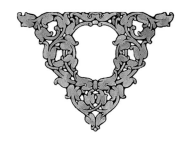

Desk stretch

You can try this short stretching routine at your desk. It's a great relaxation technique to use just before you go into an important meeting or before making that phone call you've been putting off. It is also effective if you are starting to feel stressed and tight around the back and shoulders and don't have time to get away from your desk. It only takes a few minutes to complete and will leave you feeling refreshed and centered.

1. Push your chair back until, with your back against the chair, you are at an arm's length from the desk. Sit squarely in your chair with your legs shoulder width apart and your feet flat on the floor. Close your eyes and take two or three slow, deep breaths.

2. Clasp your hands behind your back and gradually lean backwards, arching your upper back over the top of the chair. Return to the position in step 1 and take two or three deep breaths.

3. Place your palms against the edge of the desk and, keeping your back straight, press against the desk as if you were trying to push it away. Hold for a few seconds then let go. This will tighten and then relax the muscles in your arms and chest. Return to the position in step 1 and take two or three deep breaths.

4. Placing your legs together, tighten your thigh muscles and lift your legs until they are straight out in front of you with your toes flexed back towards your body. Hold for a few seconds then relax. Return to the position in step 1 and take two or three deep breaths.

After-Work Wind Down

Work problems are among the greatest contributors to stress, but the concerns of your job should not impact on your enjoyment of the rest of your life. You can learn to leave work behind.

Many of us lead hectic work lives. We travel to and from work; juggle home responsibilities, work pressures and financial commitments. It is not surprising we may find it difficult to switch off at the end of the day.

One technique to overcome this is to create a ritual for yourself that indicates your working day has finished and your recreational time has begun. This will occur at different times for different people. You may like to begin the ritual the moment you finish work. If you travel home through heavy traffic, you may want to start the ritual when you get home. If you have small children you may like to make this time after they have gone to bed. If you choose to bring work home, complete that first.

The ritual doesn't have to be dramatic or formal, just an indication you have moved from one part of the day to another. It may consist of lighting an aromatherapy burner, or changing your clothes and shoes to something loose and comfortable; the ritual may simply consist of standing in the garden for a few moments while enjoying the evening sky.

Whatever you choose, keep the ritual simple and use it each day to signify the beginning of your relaxation time.

Establishing a routine ensures sufficient time is allocated to your relaxation techniques; this is necessary if you are really going to feel the benefits.

Incorporate variety into your relaxation time — a relaxation technique will lose its effectiveness if it becomes boring or begins to feel like a chore. Find out what you enjoy most and what works best for you at particular times giving attention to your mind, your body and your emotional well-being.

A relaxation technique for the body

Use a series of stretching exercises or yoga exercises every day after work. This will help your body release the tensions stored during the day and allow your muscles to relax. As your fitness and stamina increase you may like to follow up with a long walk, a dance class one or two evenings a week, or a game of tennis or golf on the weekend.

A relaxation technique for the mind

Practice a meditation, visualization or breathing exercise every day. Even if it is only for ten minutes each day it can make a great difference to how you feel and how you sleep. If you spend most of your day indoors, try doing this exercise outside; the fresh air can also help you feel revitalized.

A relaxation technique for the emotions

Do something that you really enjoy and which will make you feel uplifted. This can be as simple as curling up in an armchair or spending an hour reading a good book. You may even like to take up a peaceful but specialized hobby like growing orchids in a hot house. Another enjoyable and relaxing experience is taking the time to have a leisurely talk with an old friend.

Bedtime Preparation

your mind. Don't drink any alcohol or caffeine during the evening; instead try a hot chamomile or lavender tea.

If, by the time you are in bed, you find your mind is still racing, try a visualization. Imagine a large room with a high ceiling, stone walls and a set of huge, thick oak doors. Place in this room all the images and words that are running through your head. Everything that comes into your head, people, problems, things to do, worries and concerns, put into the room. Close and bolt the massive doors to seal the room. Tell yourself that you will open the doors in the morning and deal with any pressing matters at that time and not before.

The following tense-relax exercise, performed while you are lying in bed, is a simple way of relaxing before sleep.

1. Lie flat on your back with your arms beside you. Take a few deep breaths and with each outward breath imagine all tension leaving your body.

2. Beginning at your feet, flex and tense them as hard as you can, hold for a few seconds and then relax.

3. Point your toes and tighten your calf muscles; hold for a few seconds, then relax.

4. Repeat this process with each set of muscles in your body, working up your legs, to your buttocks, and lower back. Tighten your back muscles by raising your shoulders up to your ears and then relaxing. Continue this process with your hands, arms and neck.

5. Finish by pulling a face with your jaw clenched and then relaxing, and another with your jaw open and then relaxing.

6. Breathe deeply keeping your focus on your breath. Check your body for any residual tension and, if you find any, tighten the area and relax once more. With each outgoing breath imagine all remaining tension leaving your body.

*D*raw yourself a warm to hot bath and add some aromatherapy oils. Play some relaxing music, lie back in the water and breathe deeply . . .

A bath is a wonderful way to end the day and prepare yourself for bed. Ensure you have done everything you need to do before your bath, then pamper yourself. Try a luxurious bubble bath every now and then if this appeals and experiment with different oil combinations. You may like to practice some visualizations in the bath, or a mini-meditation. Often, after a bath like this, sleep will descend upon you moments after you go to bed.

You may have difficulty getting to sleep because your mind keeps racing through all the events of that day or anticipates the matters of the next. If this scenario is familiar to you, avoid doing anything mentally stimulating in the hour before you go to bed. Try a meditation in preference to reading a book. Give yourself a massage instead of watching television and use this time to calm

Deep Relaxation Exercise

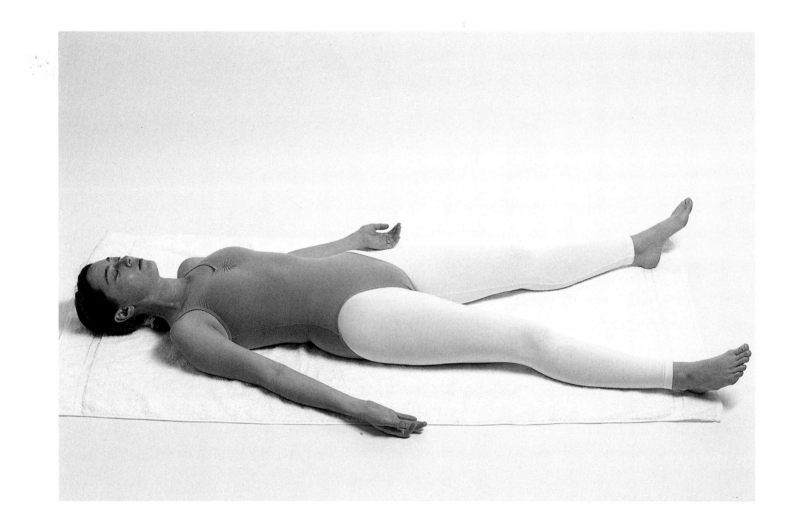

This simple exercise requires no special equipment or training,
and can easily be incorporated into your weekly routine.
By focusing on your breathing and relaxing the tension in your
muscles, you will feel the stress slip away.

*B*eing in a deeply relaxed state for 20 to 30 minutes at least two or three times a week can act as a preventative measure against becoming overly stressed and fatigued. As you practice techniques for becoming deeply relaxed you will find it easier and quicker to achieve relaxation.

Preparation

Ensure you have 20 to 30 minutes during which you will not be disturbed. Find a place in which you feel comfortable, where the light is soft or dimmed, and that is relatively quiet. Your body temperature may drop during this process, so make sure you are warmly dressed in loose clothing. If you are sensitive to the cold, you may also like to have a blanket or shawl handy to pull over you if necessary. Find a comfortable position. You may lie on your back, your head supported by a pillow or sit in a chair with your back straight; or you may prefer to sit on the floor, your back against a wall.

The exercise

1. Close your eyes and focus on your breath. Breathe deeply in through your nose to avoid drying out your mouth and throat, and exhale through your mouth. Be aware of how your breath feels as it fills your abdomen, and how it feels as you exhale and your abdomen falls.

2. With each inward breath imagine all the tension in your body collecting together, and with each outward breath imagine all this tension leaving your body. Continue to breathe deeply and evenly.

3. Now move your attention to different parts of your body. Begin with your feet. Let the floor take the full weight of your feet and feel them become heavy. Imagine them being so heavy that you couldn't possibly move them. Now become aware of your legs. They are also becoming heavy, a weight on the floor. If you notice any tension, imagine it being released with each outward breath.

4. Repeat step 3 with your concentration focusing in turn on your buttocks, stomach, back, arms and head.

There is no set amount of time for you to relax these areas of your body. Allow as much time as is necessary to feel all tension has left your muscles. Return to an area if you notice tension there at a later time.

5. Return your attention to your breath. If you find your mind wandering, try not to participate in these stray thoughts; simply observe them before returning your focus to your breath. You will find that as you become more practiced at relaxation techniques you will be able to maintain your focus more easily.

6. Bring your attention now to how you feel emotionally, and be aware of any stress you may be feeling. Try and view this stress as being separate from you and from your body. Continue breathing slowly while you observe the stress, and allow it to take on a shape and/or color.

7. When you have established an image of the stress as a separate object, slowly watch it dissolve and flow away with each breath you exhale.

8. Once you feel completely relaxed, allow yourself to stay where you are for as long as feels comfortable. Being in a deeply relaxed state can alter our sense of time. It is not unusual to feel that only a few moments have passed, when in reality you may have been relaxing for 15 or 20 minutes.

9. Give yourself time to slowly return to an ordinary, waking state. You may like to gently stretch some of your muscles while you remain sitting or lying. You should only stand up when you feel ready and any feelings of weightlessness or disorientation have passed.

Acupressure

*This ancient healing technique can be used
safely and effectively at home to treat the symptoms of stress,
from anxiety and tension to headaches.*

*A*cupuncture and acupressure have evolved from the Oriental healing arts which utilize the concepts of "Yin" and "Yang" and of "Ch'i" (or "Qi"). In Chinese philosophy, Yin and Yang represent the polarities of life. In very simple terms, Yin is the passive, feminine, cold aspect, while Yang is the active, masculine, hot aspect. Ch'i is the vital life-force energy that runs through our bodies in channels or "meridians". When we are in good health, Yin and Yang are in balance; body, mind and emotions are in harmony, and the Ch'i flows freely through our body. When an imbalance occurs, acupuncture and acupressure are healing techniques which can be applied to the points along the meridians. They aim to balance the Ch'i and relieve the symptoms of the illness.

There has been evidence of the use of acupuncture from as early as 200 BC. As it has evolved over the centuries, acupuncture has become useful in the treatment of many chronic conditions. It is often used in China as an anaesthetic during surgery. Good results have been achieved in the treatment of migraine, hypertension, sciatica and other muscular complaints as well as in treatment of substance dependencies and eating disorders. In modern times, it makes use of fine, stainless steel needles inserted painlessly beneath the skin on specific points. An acupuncturist will use a variety of diagnostic techniques including checking the "pulse" of each meridian to identify where an imbalance of energy is caused. He or she will then insert needles into the relevant points. There are hundreds of different points, each with a different function, so acupuncture should only be practiced by a fully qualified acupuncturist.

Acupressure, however, works with finger pressure on the same points, and while you should not attempt to treat yourself for a serious health problem, you can use acupressure as an effective relaxation technique at home. The individual points are named after the major organ in the corresponding meridian, or after the two "control" meridians followed by a number. The control meridians are known as the "Governing Vessel", which incorporates the spine, and the "Conception Vessel" which runs down the middle of the front of the body.

How to apply acupressure

Acupressure can be applied either on bare skin or through loose clothing. Try and maintain a light focus on your breathing throughout, ensuring that it is smooth and even.

There are three different types of pressure applied in acupressure in accordance with the desired change in the Ch'i. If the Ch'i is deficient, it is increased by applying firm, stationary pressure to the acupressure point for one or two minutes. If the Ch'i is blocked, it is dispersed by making firm circular movements with thumb or fingers at the acupressure point for about one or two minutes. If there is excess Ch'i, it is calmed by placing the hand, palm face down, over the acupressure point and holding it there for one or two minutes.

WHEN TO AVOID ACUPRESSURE

There are certain times when acupressure is inappropriate.
Do not apply pressure to
• scar tissue • an area where the skin is broken
• swollen or inflamed areas • varicose veins

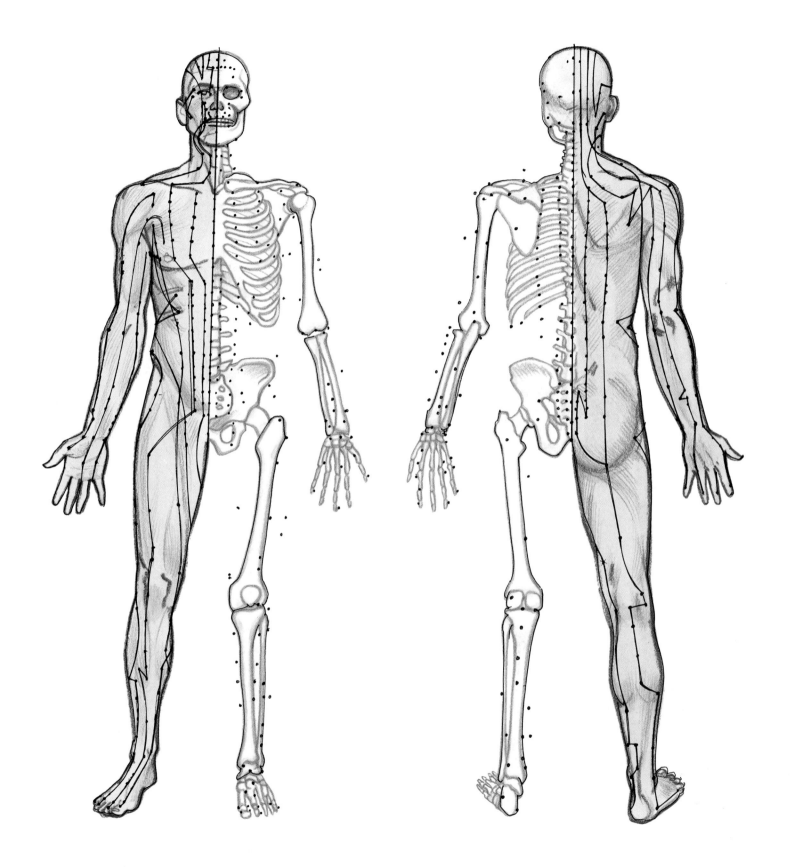

Meridian system — front view   **Meridian system — back view**

large intestine 4

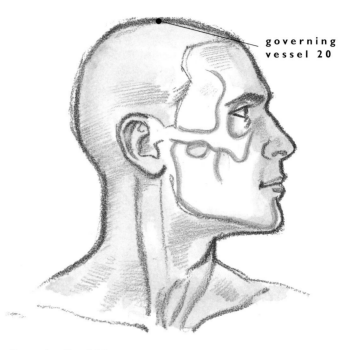

governing vessel 20

Acupressure points for relaxation

For releasing tension

Large Intestine 4

This point is in the fleshy part between your thumb and index finger. It is useful for releasing muscular tension around the neck and shoulders and can be very tender if you have a tension headache. Use circular movements to disperse the Ch'i.

   Do not use this point during pregnancy.

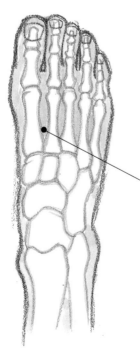

liver 3

Liver 3

This point is on the hollow where the bones of the big toe and the second toe meet. Using the tip of your thumb, disperse the Ch'i with small circular movements.

Governing Vessel 20

This point is at the very top of the head at a mid-point between the ears. Use the pad of your thumb to disperse the Ch'i.

   Do not use this point if you have high blood pressure.

For tension headaches

Gall Bladder 20.

This point is at the base of the skull; it is the hollow formed between the neck muscles. Use the pad of your thumb to gently disperse the Ch'i. Be gentle as this point may be very sensitive.

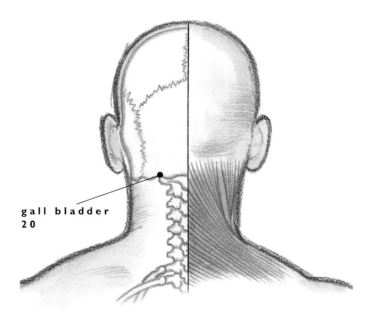

gall bladder 20

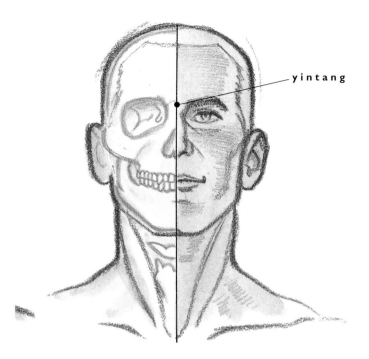

Heart 7

Heart 7
This point is at the small hollow where your wrist meets your hand on the little finger side. Calm the Ch'i at this point by lightly stroking your thumb over it. Do not apply any pressure.

Heart 6

Heart 7

Conception Vessel 12 and 14
To find CV12 imagine a line running down the middle of your body, and on this line measure five finger widths above your navel. Calm this area by placing your hand, palm down, over the point and focus on your breathing. Repeat this with CV14 which is 8 finger widths above your navel on the mid-line.

yintang

Yintang
This point is at the top of the nose, between the eyebrows. Gently disperse the Ch'i at this point with the pad of one of your middle fingers.

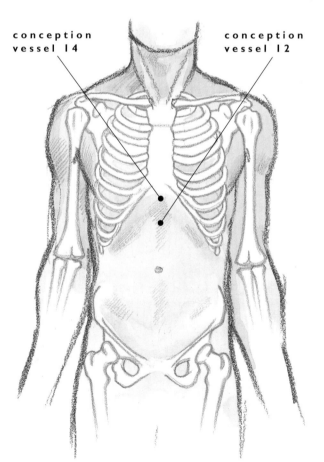

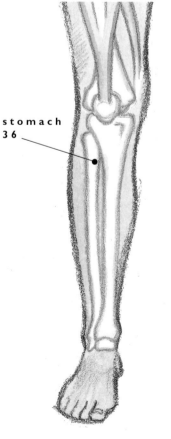

Stomach 36
To find this point measure four finger widths down from your kneecap towards the outside of your leg. Stimulate the Ch'i at this point with firm, stationary pressure.

For worry, fear and anxiety

Heart Protector 6
This point is two finger widths down your wrist (when your palm is facing upwards) and is in the center of your forearm. Calm the Ch'i at this point by lightly stroking over it with your fingertips.

stomach 36

conception vessel 14

conception vessel 12

Aromatherapy

Essential oils extracted from the seeds, leaves, flowers, barks, gums and roots of plants have been used therapeutically since ancient times. Aromatherapy is the modern day rediscovery of these practices. The use of essential oils can have beneficial effects physically and psychologically and provide the opportunity for some very pleasant relaxation techniques.

The oils may be used in a variety of ways to help reduce stress and tension. Some are particularly suitable for relaxation, and will help induce sleep, while others are rejuvenating and uplifting.

Aromatherapy baths

Baths are often associated with lying back and letting the cares of the day slip away. Being immersed in warm water is in itself relaxing and the use of aromatherapy can make a bath even more effective as a relaxation technique. Your choice of oils should take into account whether you want to be relaxed and alert, ready to carry on with the day, or whether you intend to sleep shortly after your bath. Experiment with the oils to discover which combinations you enjoy and find most effective.

After filling your bath, simply add 4 to 12 drops of the oil or combination of oils you have selected and agitate the water to disperse the oil through the bath so that it does not cause irritation to your skin. Or you may like to use a commercial bath lotion or soap that contains suitable essential oils.

To take full advantage of the effects of an aromatherapy bath, it is worth spending a little time in preparation. Make sure you will not be disturbed for 20 to 30 minutes and that you have your thickest, fluffiest towel or a towelling bathrobe ready. A few candles will provide a warm glow of light and relaxation music will add to the effect (see the chapter on Music). Ensure you will be comfortable, with a "bath pillow" or rolled towel to support your head, and make the decision that this time is just for you and only for relaxation.

For a relaxing bath before bed

The water should be as hot as is comfortable. This will help your muscles relax and encourage the pores in your skin to open, allowing absorption of the aromatherapy oils. The heat will also vaporize the oils, making inhalation possible.

A few oil combination suggestionss:

> *Bergamot 6 drops*
> *Lavender 3 drops*
> *Sandalwood 3 drops*

> *Lemon 6 drops*
> *Ylang Ylang 3 drops*
> *Cedarwood 3 drops*

> *Clary Sage 3 drops*
> *Orange 3 drops*
> *Lavender 3 drops*

For a relaxing yet rejuvenating bath:

Fill the bath with warm, but not hot, water and use cool water to rinse your body before drying. If you are listening to music during your bath, you may like to choose a piece from the "focusing music" list to keep you relaxed yet alert (see page 50).

You can experiment with stimulating oils in the bath such as lime, cypress, and rosemary. Here are a few oil combination suggestions for rejuvenating baths:

> *Rosemary 6 drops*
> *Peppermint 3 drops*
> *Juniper 3 drops*

> *Eucalyptus 6 drops*
> *Lemon 3 drops*
> *Cypress 3 drops*

> *Bergamot 6 drops*
> *Basil 3 drops*
> *Rosemary 3 drops*

*Bath soaps, candles,
cosmetics and massage oils
can be bought already impregnated
with aromatherapy oils.
For therapeutic effect,
ensure quality essential oils,
not just fragrant oils,
have been used.*

Foot baths

Using warm to hot water in a large bowl, add 4 to 8 drops of essential oils. Soak feet for 15 minutes. This can also be a perfect time to meditate or use some auto-suggestions to relax more deeply (see chapters Attitude and Meditation).

Compresses

Cold compresses are very useful to relieve headaches caused by tension and stress. Fill a bowl with ice cold water, add 6 to 10 drops of essential oil and disperse through the water. Place a cloth in the water, then wring out the excess. Place on the forehead and temples for about 20 minutes. Lavender oil works effectively or try a combination such as 4 drops of lavender, 2 drops of orange and 2 drops of chamomile.

A NOTE OF CAUTION

Essential oils are pure and concentrated. Except for lavender and tea tree, the oils should not be applied undiluted to the skin. While most oils are safe to use, some (including basil, cedarwood, clary sage, hyssop, juniper, marjoram, pennyroyal, sage and thyme) should be avoided during pregnancy. Other oils (such as bergamot and lemon) are phototoxic and should not be used on the skin when it is exposed to sunlight. If you are unsure of the use of any oil, or are prone to allergic reactions, are pregnant, or suffer from high blood pressure, epilepsy or another neural disorder it is best to consult a professional aromatherapist and medical practitioner before using aromatherapy.

Relaxing essential oils

*Chamomile
Cedarwood
Clary Sage
Frankincense
Lavender
Neroli
Rose
Sandalwood
Ylang ylang*

Uplifting essential oils

*Basil
Bergamot
Cypress
Eucalyptus
Geranium
Juniper
Lemon
Lemongrass
Orange
Patchouli
Peppermint
Rosemary*

One effective way of using
essential oils is in
an aromatherapy inhalation.
Fill a bowl with very hot water,
add 6 to 10 drops of suitable oils
(see below) and,
holding a towel over your head,
breathe in the
fragrance-filled steam.

Vaporizers

Vaporizers, also known as fragrancers, burners, aroma lamps
and diffusers, can fill the air with fragrance and assist you
in remaining relaxed and focused throughout your day.
Choose one with a reasonably deep "well" if you are
planning to burn oils for a few hours as it is important there
is always some water in the bowl.

After filling the bowl of the vaporizer with water, add
3 to 10 drops of essential oil and place a candle underneath
the bowl. Check the water level occasionally and top up as
needed. One suggestion for a day when you need to be
mentally focused is a blend of 6 drops of lemon, 3 drops
of rosemary and 3 drops of basil.

Aromatherapy massage

An aromatherapy massage from a qualified aromatherapist
is an indulgent relaxation technique that will leave you
feeling pampered and nurtured. Your muscles are
relaxed, your circulation is improved by the massage
and the essential oils are absorbed through the skin.
A professional aromatherapist will consult with you and
blend a combination of oils specific to your situation;
however it is also possible for you to use essential oils when
you are giving yourself a massage (see chapter on Massage).
Use a good quality oil like sweet almond or avocado as
a "carrier" oil to which you can add a few drops of
essential oils.

Aromatherapy pillows

For a sleep pillow, mix dried lavender flowers and dried
rose petals, then add 4 drops of cedarwood and 2 drops of
orange essential oils. Use this mix to fill a drawstring bag
made from cheesecloth, muslin or thin cotton. Place this
"pillow" between your usual pillow and pillowcase. These
relaxing oils should help induce a restful and fragrant sleep.

For an eye pillow, cut two pieces of cotton material,
each approximately 10 inches (25 cm) long and 4 inches
(10 cm) wide. Sew the two rectangles together on three
sides. Turn this inside out to make a pouch and fill with
linseed (available from health food stores). Add 2 drops
of bergamot, 1 drop of lavender and 1 drop of orange
essential oils. Sew the pouch closed.

Drape this pillow across your eyes when you are
relaxing. It can also be placed across your forehead to
soothe a tension headache.

Inhalations

Breathing in essential oils can help relieve mental fatigue
and aid in maintaining a relaxed, clear mind. You can use
a towel and a bowl of water (see above) or, for a quicker
alternative, saturate a cloth with very hot water and add
1 to 3 drops of an essential oil. Hold the cloth against your
face and breathe deeply two or three times. Try 1 drop of
lavender and 1 drop of neroli as a calming inhalation or
2 drops of bergamot and 1 drop of cypress as a pick-me-up.

Vaporizers can be used throughout the day, in your home or workplace,
to help you relax or focus, depending on the oils you choose.
If you change oils, make sure to wipe out the bowl in between uses.

Attitude

*Just as our emotional and
mental states can be
the cause of stress,
our minds and our imaginations
can be the source of healing,
peace and relaxation.*

One of the most effective ways to develop
a more relaxed and peaceful lifestyle is to
become aware of our attitudes and beliefs
and how these relate to the way we deal with stress and
stressful events.

If we analyse our reactions, we will see that we don't
always act rationally. Often we act on well established, but
inappropriate, beliefs. For example, on an intellectual level
we may know that if we make a mistake it is better to face
up to it immediately, take responsibility and deal with the
consequences. People who avoid taking responsibility,
who attempt to hide the problem or push the blame onto
someone else, create situations fraught with fear, anxiety
and guilt that span days instead of an awkward half hour.

Recognizing the beliefs behind our actions is the first
step in changing the way we behave. When faced with a
potentially stressful situation, you should try to distance
yourself from the event for a moment. Ask yourself what
action you need to take to deal with the event effectively
and remain focused and relaxed. By accepting we have a
choice to be stressed or relaxed, we give ourselves the
power to choose to remain calm.

There are a variety of techniques you can employ to
change your attitudes, improve your ability to relax quickly
and easily, and to remain calm, avoiding frequent stress.

Visualization

A very simple and effective relaxation technique,
visualization is, in simple terms, conscious day-dreaming.
As you practice visualization, these day-dreams will become
more vivid, and the time it takes you to achieve relaxation
will become shorter.

Our imaginations are powerful tools. Just as we can work
our bodies into a "fight or flight" response by thinking
about a stressful incident, we can also create a state of deep
relaxation by thinking about a calm and peaceful situation.

Visualization can counter negative thoughts, anxiety
and nervousness. This process of creating scenarios in our
minds, in which we react as we would like to react, can
assist in building confidence to deal with challenges; it also
provides alternative ways to cope with recurring events that
are stressful to us.

A visualization for deep relaxation
Relaxation visualization is effective only if its images
are relaxing to you. The following is an example only;
the most effective visualizations will be the ones you
develop yourself.

When you begin to practice visualization, choose a quiet
place where you are unlikely to be disturbed, close your
eyes and take a few deep breaths. Once you become more
familiar with the techniques, you will find that noises and
interruptions become less of a distraction.

Imagine yourself on a white sandy beach, the day clear
and warm. You are wearing loose cotton clothing and lying
on a thick towel on the sand. Try and incorporate all your
senses into this image. Be aware of how the towel feels
against your skin and the difference between this texture
and that of the clothing touching your skin. In this vivid
mental image, place your hands on your thighs and feel
how warm they are from the sun's rays. Appreciate the
vibrant colors of the sea and sky and their contrast with
the silvery white of the sand. Run your fingers through the
sand beside you and feel how the top layer is fine, warm
and dry; while the layer of sand below is cooler and slightly
damp. See and feel how some of the grains of sand cling to
your hands. Smell the seaweed drying on the beach and
taste the slightly salty air. Hear the rhythmic sound of the
waves breaking on the beach. Be aware of how completely
mentally and physically relaxed you are in this image.

Vizualizations for deep relaxation are most effective when you develop them yourself, selecting images and sensations that are relaxing to you personally. Peaceful natural settings can be ideal starting points for these mental journeys.

A visualization for a stressful situation
If there is an event approaching that you feel nervous and anxious about, it will help to develop a visualization about this event. The length of time it takes to do this will depend on how stressful the event is to you. You may like to come back to it on a few occasions until you can complete the visualization from beginning to end without feeling stressed.

Again, try and incorporate taste, touch, smell, sound and vision into the visualization. Begin with images just before the anticipated event. In your mind's eye, look at the room around you; notice what you are wearing and how the fabric feels; smell the room, hear the sounds. Once you have established this image, slowly work through the event, including all moments that cause you concern.

If at any time you are not progressing as you would like to or negative mind-chatter begins to creep in, simply stop and begin again at whichever point you feel comfortable. If you begin to feel anxious, distance yourself from the image for a moment and take a few deep breaths. You may decide to finish the session at this point or begin again once you have relaxed.

AUTO-SUGGESTION AND AFFIRMATIONS

Auto-suggestion and affirmations both work on the verbal or mental
repetition of a positive phrase that states — as though it is fact
— your situation as you would like to experience it.
The emphasis in auto-suggestion is to repeat the phrase while
in a deeply relaxed state, thus allowing the subconscious mind to
absorb the meaning of the phrase and create change in
behavioral and belief patterns.
The principle of affirmations is based on the concept
that you create your own environment by how you think.
You are therefore more likely to achieve your goals if you
think positively than if you dwell on the negative.
Affirmations can be used at any time, whether you are deeply relaxed or not.
They also act as reminders of your goals or your desired states of being.

To be effective, the phrases you use should be:
• specific — contemplate what it is you want
• in the present tense
• in the first person — use "I"
• positive — state what you want, not what you don't want
• repeated — either in your mind, audibly or
by writing it down.
Examples of affirmations/auto-suggestions for relaxation include:
• "I remain relaxed and calm throughout the day."
• "I choose to work in a relaxed and peaceful manner."
• "I am more than capable of dealing with today's challenges."
• "I am confident and relaxed."

*Auto-suggestions and affirmations can be used with
other relaxation techniques, such as during a bath or
while practicing meditation or breathing exercises.*

Self-hypnosis

Used in the treatment of many physical and emotional ailments, self-hypnosis can be particularly useful as a relaxation technique. Many people find the easiest way to use self-hypnosis is to first visit a qualified hypnotherapist for an introductory session or two. The hypnotherapist will take you through the process of achieving a trance state and provide you with scripts that are specifically tailored to your individual needs. These scripts will contain the messages you wish to implant in your subconscious mind to effect relaxation. With this background you are then able to continue your hypnosis sessions alone.

First, consider why you are using self-hypnosis. Are you wanting to sleep more soundly through the night? Perhaps you are wanting to maintain a relaxed state when you are in a business meeting? When you are certain of your purpose write down and memorize two or three affirmations. You will use these once you have attained a trance state. Read through the following steps a few times so that you are completely familiar with what you are going to do. You may like to make a tape of the process of going into a trance, the affirmations and the de-hypnotizing process to play to yourself during these sessions.

To reach a trance state find a comfortable chair to sit in with your feet flat on the floor and your arms resting loosely in your lap. Make sure the room is not too bright and that you will not be disturbed.

1. Begin by focusing on your breathing until it becomes deep, smooth and even.

2. Tell yourself you will go into a light trance and stay in that state for ten minutes (or a shorter time to suit) and then you will bring yourself back out of the trance. Remind yourself that you are perfectly able to bring yourself out of the trance before that time if you need to, and that you will not fall into a deep trance state.

3. Then close your eyes and imagine you are climbing down a wide spiral staircase. There are twenty steps, and with each inward breath you take a step downwards and with each breath out you release tension and become more relaxed.

4. Notice as you go down the staircase that your whole body, from the tip of your toes to the top of your head, is feeling heavier and heavier. Soon you become so relaxed you couldn't possibly move, not even to open your eyes. You are now in a light trance.

5. Repeat your affirmations to yourself.

6. Having repeated your affirmations allow yourself time to just be still and relaxed.

7. Bring yourself out of the trance by beginning the climb back up the staircase. With each inward breath, feel yourself becoming aware of your body, feel it become lighter. With each breath out, take another step upwards. By the time you reach the top you will be out of the trance, feeling peaceful yet alert.

CAUTION

It is possible to try self-hypnosis by yourself at home for relaxation without visiting a professional; however hypnosis is a powerful tool and there are a few warnings that should be heeded

• Do not use the techniques on another person.

• Do not use self-hypnosis if you have any history of emotional or mental instability.

• Always use a de-hypnotizing process at the end of the session.

• Do not attempt to resolve serious behavioral or emotional problems without first consulting with a professional

Making choices

For many people the list of things they "must" or "should" do creates enough pressure to keep them constantly stressed. If you feel this applies to you, try a simple technique to reduce stress.

First, acknowledge you have choice in whether or not you will do something. This alone can relieve the feeling of being weighed down by demands made on you. Then try saying "I choose to..." rather than "I must..." or say "I want to..." rather than "I should..."

When you make a conscious choice to complete tasks, you become motivated to do so. This also includes learning to say "no" when you are asked to do something you feel is outside your responsibilities or which will place unreasonable demands on your time. Saying "yes" when you want to say "no" is likely to make you resentful and angry and is unlikely to reduce your stress levels. If you generally say "yes" to any request, those around you may initially react to your refusals; however, if you keep calm and polite they will gradually come to respect your redefined boundaries.

Breathing Techniques

*B*reathing is fundamental to our health. Apart from the obvious fact that it is impossible for us to live without breathing, the way we breathe can have dramatic effects on the way our bodies operate and the way we feel.

When we inhale, we are taking air into our lungs; the blood vessels in the lungs absorb the oxygen which the blood transports around the body. At the same time, the blood releases carbon dioxide into the air within the lungs and this waste product is then exhaled. The balance of oxygen absorbed and carbon dioxide expelled is the key to effective breathing. Shallow breathing can result in too little oxygen being absorbed, thus depriving the cells in our bodies of oxygen and leaving a surplus of carbon dioxide in the lung tissue. Hyperventilation can cause the body to expel too much carbon dioxide producing dizziness, sweating and palpitations. This often leads to increased anxiety and results in even faster breathing, worsening the effects.

The good news is that learning to breathe properly is not difficult, although it will take practice before it becomes your usual breathing pattern.

Breathing is one of the most effective and most practical relaxation techniques. Once you are familiar with the exercises they can be practiced quickly and effectively at any time, even if you only have a few minutes to spare.

Step 1

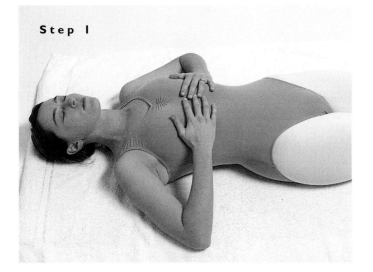

Step 2

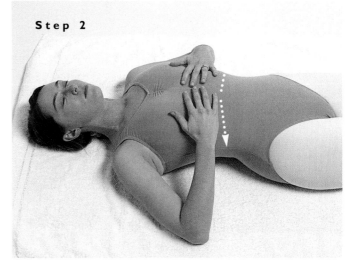

Deep breathing exercise

The first step in learning to breathe properly is to become aware of how you are breathing now. To do this, place one hand on your chest and the other over your abdomen. Now take a deep breath. Which hand moves? If your stomach fills with air and your hand moved outwards, you are using your diaphragm correctly. If the hand on your chest moved outwards, you are using your upper chest and body to breathe and limiting your lung capacity.

The diaphragm is a strong sheet of muscle tissue that forms the floor of the chest cavity. When we inhale properly it contracts downwards towards the abdomen while the muscles between each rib spread the rib cage providing a larger space for the lungs to expand.

It is easiest to first practice correct breathing lying down. Once you have become comfortable with the technique you will be able to use it standing, sitting or when walking and exercising. Remove any tight or uncomfortable clothing and support your head with a rolled towel making sure the support is not too high and keeping your airways straight.

1. Place your hands at the bottom of your rib cage. This keeps your attention on how you are breathing. It may take a few breaths before you feel comfortable with this technique, so don't become anxious and concerned about doing it right the first time. If you become light-headed return to your normal breathing for a few moments then try again.

2. Inhale through your nose and, breathing slowly and deeply, try and fill your abdominal cavity with air. Try not to move your shoulders or puff out your chest.

3. Exhale through your mouth and feel your abdominal muscles fall. If you also feel your shoulders fall, it means that you lifted them while inhaling. Be aware of this and try not to lift them with your next breath.

4. Repeat this step several times until you feel comfortable with the rhythm. On each exhalation imagine all the tension in your body leaving with your breath.

5. Finish by returning to a normal depth of breathing but try to maintain the style of breathing.

6. Rise slowly.

By placing your hands on your abdomen as you breathe, you will be able to feel your abdomen expand, causing your hands to move outwards. Effective breathing comes from the diaphram, not the chest.

29

Sectional Breathing Step 1

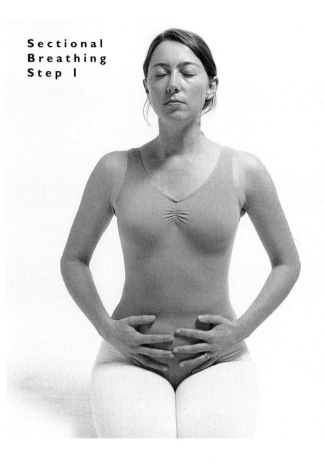

Sectional Breathing Step 3

Sectional breathing exercise

This exercise will further increase your awareness of how you breathe. Once you have become familiar with this exercise you will find it useful as an almost instant stress reliever. On a long term basis, this exercise can improve your digestion, reduce muscular tension in the shoulder and neck areas and increase your lung capacity.

1. Place your hands over your lower abdomen. Breathe slowly in through your nose, focusing on filling your lower abdomen and pelvic area with air. Exhale slowly and as fully as possible through your mouth.

2. Repeat this for another six breaths.

3. Move your hands to the lower half of your rib cage. Make sure your shoulders are relaxed and take seven breaths in through your nose and out through your mouth focusing on expanding your rib cage with every inhalation.

4. Rest your fingers on your collar bone (see opposite). Focusing on expanding the upper chest and shoulder area, without moving your shoulders upwards, take seven deep breaths in through the nose and out through the mouth.

5. Now take seven long, deep breaths and fill all three areas with each breath, then feel these areas contract as you exhale.

6. Return to normal breathing and remain seated for a few minutes.

Exhalation exercise

This is a different type of exercise because, rather than focusing on breathing in, it concentrates on expelling as much air as possible during exhalation; thus inhalation becomes a reflex action. It is also a useful exercise to relieve stress as the movement of your body helps release physical and emotional tensions.

1. Stand with your feet shoulder width apart and arms hanging loosely by your sides. Bring your arms up in front of you as you take a deep breath in.

2. Make a loud "haaaa" or "oooo" sound and at the same time bend your knees and allow your upper body to become limp and flop over, your head ending up near your knees. As the top half of your body falls forward, your arms should swing down freely. Expel as much air as possible repeating the "haaaa" or "oooo" sound if necessary.

3. Take a deep breath in as you slowly rise back to a standing position.

4. Take two or three normal breaths so that you don't get dizzy and then repeat.

Sectional
Breathing
Step 4

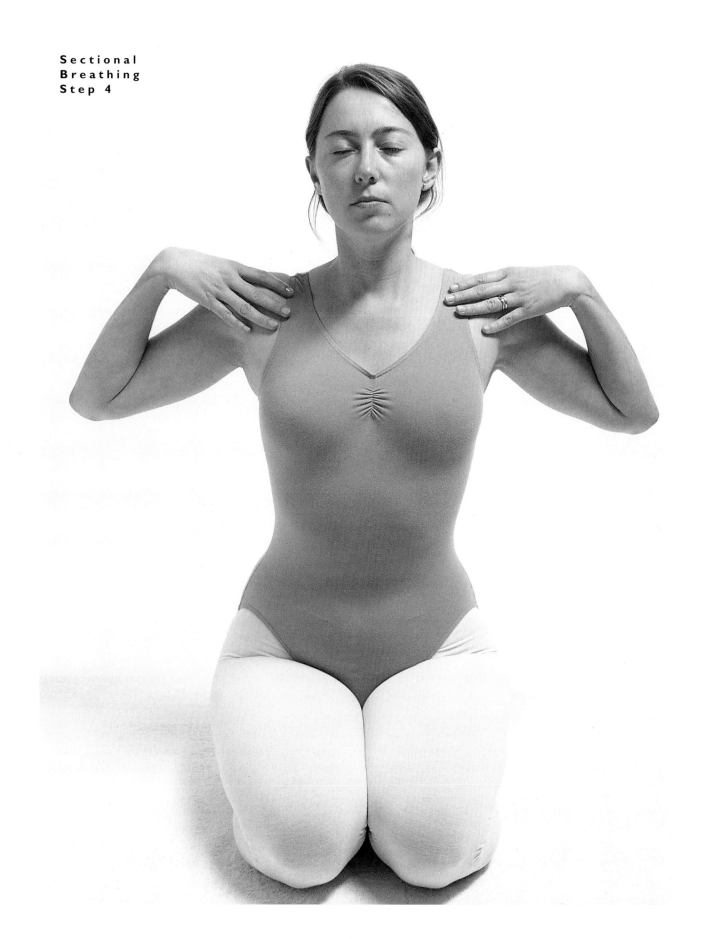

Color

It may seem surprising but the colors that surround us and those that we wear can have a significant impact on the way we feel.

olor surrounds us. It is in the clothes we wear and around us in the rooms in which we spend time. There are myriad colors in nature as well as in the created environment of our town.
We may be attracted to paintings, photographs, ornaments and artworks because of their colors.

The colors we choose to have around us have psychological and physical effects and can influence our emotions, our stress levels, our blood pressure and the way in which we perceive our environment.

These factors have been utilized by marketing companies wanting to sell more product, prison systems wanting to control behavior and by companies wanting to increase the efficiency of their work force. They can also be used to help us feel more relaxed, increase our ability to focus, or feel more energetic. How color affects our health and our mood is a subject to which some people devote many years of study; however there are some easy guidelines that can be followed for choices of color in your environment.

When choosing a color scheme for a room, the purpose of the room should be taken into consideration. The intensity and amount of the color used also needs to be addressed. Imagine, for example, a room in which all four walls are painted a deep crimson. For most people, being in this room would be overwhelming and uncomfortable, yet red used in much smaller doses can bring warmth and vitality.

As a rule, paler shades of a color will be more relaxing than darker shades when used for interiors. Dark shades can become oppressive and reduce the perceived amount of space in a room. Even in clothes, white and very pale shades in clothes are believed by many to be the most effective for relaxation.

Experiment with wearing different colors, taking notice of how you feel when you are wearing each one. Dress to suit your moods and energy levels. Be aware of how different you feel when wearing a bright red shirt on a bleak, overcast day to wearing red when the weather is hot and humid.

Red		Red is stimulating and increases the appetite — a good choice for a kitchen, but not for a room in which you would like to relax or sleep. Red has been shown to increase blood pressure. It can be helpful in lifting spirits — try wearing something red when you feel you need a boost. Adding white to red softens the effects of red and results in peaceful, soothing pinks.
Orange		Orange has similar qualities to red. It is stimulating, it increases the appetite and can also help to create a warm, comfortable environment. Orange, like red, can be overpowering so is best used in small quantities.
Yellow		Yellow is emotionally uplifting. It helps us concentrate and stimulates the mind, making it perfect when incorporated into an office or work-room, but not into a bedroom as you are likely to be too stimulated to sleep.
Green		Green has soothing qualities which makes it suitable for most types of rooms, whether in wallpaint or furnishings or the green of indoor plants. Wearing green can be calming on days when you feel stressed or anxious.
Blue		Blue is gentle and relaxing, and creates a feeling of space. Blue will give a room a calming atmosphere; it has the opposite effect to red and can be used to lower blood pressure. Pale blue is a wonderful choice for a bedroom or any other room in which you unwind and wearing blue may help you feel calmer and less agitated.
Purple		Purple has similar properties to blue. Pale purple and lavenders create a peaceful relaxing feeling. Darker shades of purple are also restful but should be used in smaller amounts as they can become depressing. Because purple contains red, it can also bring warmth to an area.
Black		Light is reflected with the least energy from a black object. Used in excess black can be overpowering, depressing, and give the feeling of immutability. Business people often wear black to create an impression of power and control.
White		White objects reflect light with the greatest energy and so create a feeling of space and peace. White can, however, give a room a cold, clinical feeling, but the clever use of other colors will alleviate this. Wearing white helps you to be relaxed and alert at the same time.

Exercise

You can experience the benefits of regular exercise without expensive equipment or gym membership.

Regular exercise is vital to maintaining a healthy and relaxed lifestyle. It does not need to be vigorous or strenuous exercise, and it is always wise to begin with a little and gradually build — but it does need to be regular.

If you haven't exercised for a long time, choose a gentle form of exercise that you know will fit easily with your routine. The benefits of exercise take a little while to become apparent so it is unrealistic to expect yourself suddenly transformed into a dedicated athlete. As you feel the benefits, and doing more becomes easier, try and vary the type of exercise you do. This will not only stop you getting bored with the routine, but will also enable you to exercise different muscle groups.

Walking

Walking is an ideal form of exercise as it doesn't matter what your fitness level is when you begin. It is also gentle on your joints, although a good pair of sport shoes is essential to protect your knees, ankles and lower back from undue strain. Start with a pace and distance that are comfortable for you and gradually increase both so that you are doing a little more each day. Explore your local area to find peaceful walks and take advantage of any parks or open areas. Avoid any area that has heavy traffic as the effect of inhaling car fumes will outweigh any benefit you gain from walking.

A brisk walk first thing in the morning can be a great way to wake yourself up — you may also enjoy the beauty of a sunrise and the peacefulness of bird song. Use your walking time to practice breathing correctly and regard this as a "worry-free" time. If you get into this sort of routine you will soon find that you miss the walk if you don't do it.

Stretching

Stretching is a must before beginning any sort of exercise; it can also be beneficial as an exercise routine to reduce stress and tension, and to promote relaxation. Stretching, as part of a regular routine, will improve your flexibility, strength and stamina; it improves circulation and helps your body to eliminate waste products more effectively. Develop a routine and try and practice it every day as part of your relaxation program.

1. Begin each session by standing with feet shoulder width apart, knees very slightly bent, arms hanging loosely by your side and torso straight. Make sure your weight is evenly distributed over your legs. Take a few deep breaths in this position.

2. Straighten your legs and lock your knees; lift one leg up and flex your toes back toward your leg, then point them away from you. Repeat this three or four times. Then, gently and slowly, rotate your foot around the ankle. Repeat this three or four times. Repeat this whole step with the other foot. (See previous page.)

Step 3

Step 5

3. With arms by your side, turn them so that the palms are facing outward, taking a deep breath in, slowly raise your arms until your palms are facing each other above your head. Exhale and return your arms to your sides. Repeat three or four times.

4. Bring your arms above your head as in step 3, but this time stretch with one arm as high as you can while pulling down the opposite shoulder. Repeat with the other arm. This can be a useful stretch to release tension around the shoulders and upper back.

5. To stretch your right side widen your stance slightly and, breathing in, let your left hand slide down the length of your leg while you bring your right arm up and over your head. Exhale and return your right arm to your side. It is very important to keep your body in line during this exercise; if you lean forward you will not feel the stretch. Repeat this exercise stretching your left side.

6. Repeat steps 4 and 5 three or four times.

Step 7

Step 8

It is important to remember your breathing as you exercise.

Step 11

7. Keeping your stance wide, bend your knees and balance your upper body over your hips. With palms facing inward, inhale and raise your arms to shoulder height.

8. Exhale as you bring your hands in front of your chest, keeping arms at shoulder level. As you inhale, twist your upper body at the waist, first to the right, leading with the right arm.

9. Return to center and exhale, then inhale as you repeat, twisting to the left leading with the left arm. Return to the center and exhale. Inhale as you move your hands out again and exhale as you lower your arms to your sides.

10. Repeat steps 8 and 9 three or four times.

11. Stand with feet shoulder width apart with your right foot facing forward and your left foot at a right angle to your right foot. With your right foot, take a large step forward and bend your knee. While keeping your upper body straight and your weight evenly distributed over your hips you should be able to feel the stretch along your inner thigh.

12. Repeat step 11 using your left leg to step forward.

Step 13

Step 18

Step 14

Step 19

Step 15

Step 21

13. Lie on your back with arms down beside you and palms flat on the ground. Raise your legs and move them as though you were riding a bicycle.

14. Now sit up with one leg stretched out in front of you and the other leg bent with your foot behind your thigh.

15. Slowly slide your hands down your leg, stretching your upper body along the top of your leg. Don't force your stretch; after practicing this exercise for a few weeks, you will be amazed at how much further you can stretch.

16. Repeat step 15 with the other leg.

17. Next, stretch both legs out in front of you making a "V" shape, as wide as you comfortably can. Keeping this position gently flex and point your feet a few times.

18. Taking a deep breath in, raise your hands above your head with palms facing inwards.

19. As you exhale, lower your upper body over your leg, and grasp the ankle (or your leg as close to your ankle as you can), taking your nose as close as you can to your knee.

20. Inhale and stretch back up to center, exhale and grasp the other ankle and repeat step 19.

21. Bring one leg towards the other and turn so that you are lying on your hip. Support your upper body with your elbow and make sure the length of your body is straight — if your upper body leans forward you won't get the full benefit of this exercise. Now raise your top leg, with your foot flexed towards your upper body. Repeat these movements as many times as feels comfortable, gradually increasing the number as time goes on.

22. Repeat step 21 with the other leg.

23. Lie on your stomach with your arms clasped loosely behind your back. Pull your arms back, raising your shoulders and chest from the floor and, at the same time, clench your buttocks and raise your legs from the floor so that your body arches. Count to three and then relax. Repeat five or six times.

24. Move into a sitting position and, taking one arm over your shoulder and the other arm behind your back, clasp your hands behind your back (as pictured on page 34). Hold for five or six seconds and release. Rest for a moment and repeat with arms in the opposite position. If you are unable to clasp your hands behind your back, try the following as an alternative. Take your left arm over your shoulder and, with your right hand, clasp your left elbow. Push very gently downwards until you feel a stretch in your arm and shoulder muscles. Repeat with the right arm.

25. To finish your routine, stand up and loosely shake each limb in turn then take a few deep relaxing breaths.

Dancing

If you can allow yourself to dance without inhibition it can be a very effective means of self-expression and relaxation. Dancing increases your circulation, which supplies the body with extra oxygen and assists the elimination of wastes. It can also stimulate the release of endorphins into the body, increasing the sense of physical and emotional well-being. Over a period of time, regular dancing should increase your flexibility and stamina.

Choose music you enjoy and which suits your mood or purpose. South American rhythms are effective in recharging your energy levels; ambient music, and some classical music, lends itself to gentle, fluid movement, while rock music or rousing orchestral music may be suitable choices to express deep-felt passions or even anger and rage. Begin with smooth, slow movements until your muscles have had a chance to warm up, then move in whatever way feels right to you at that particular time. Try not to be concerned with executing dance steps or by your appearance as you dance.

You don't have to dance for very long to feel the benefits; even a few minutes can significantly alter how you feel.

Eye exercises

After many years of practice as a leading eye physician, Dr William Bates (1860-1931) came to the conclusion that stress had a detrimental effect on our vision; he believed that many of the headaches suffered by his patients were the result of too much stress. Many of the exercises he advocated are very simple to practice.

Palming

Cup the palms of your hands over your eyes with your fingertips lying in a cross on your forehead so that your eyes are in complete darkness. Keep your eyes open and leave your hands in place for at least five minutes. Breathe deeply and slowly during this process. You may notice that colors appear to be brighter and more vibrant after your eyes have been rested.

Shifting focus

Focus your vision on an object 1 to 2 feet (30 to 60 cms) away and hold for about a minute. Now shift your focus to an object approximately 20 feet (7 m) away and hold for a minute. Repeat three or four times. This is an excellent exercise if you do a lot of close-up work or if you work on a computer. Ideally, put this exercise into practice once an hour while you are working — also use this time to take a few deep breaths.

Herbs

Throughout the ages, almost every culture in the world has had a tradition of using plants for health and healing. Texts detailing the use of herbs as medicine have been discovered from the ancient civilizations in Egypt and the Middle East, Greece, Rome and China. The study of plants and their therapeutic use continues to develop and expand today as scientific research combines with knowledge collected and recorded over centuries. Like many natural therapies, the aim of herbal medicine is to put the body back into balance and allow it to heal itself. Though the principles of herbal medicine are concerned with healing over a period of time, herbal remedies will often have quite rapid and noticeable effects on the symptoms of a condition. For specific health problems a herbal medicine practitioner should be consulted; there are, however, many herbal remedies effective in reducing stress, which are as easy to use as making a cup of tea.

Infusions and teas

Teas are made by steeping the leaves, flowers, fruit, stems or seeds of a plant in boiling water for a few minutes. An infusion is generally much stronger than a tea and is made by steeping the herbs in hot or cold oil or water for anything from a few minutes to weeks.

- *Chamomile* — made from the flowers of the herb, this tea is useful for the relief of tension headaches; it is also a relaxing drink before bed. Adding the strained tea to a hot bath will help relax muscles and reduce fatigue.

- *Valerian root* — very effective if your stress is preventing you from sleeping soundly as valerian tea acts to soothe the nervous system. This herb has a rather unpleasant taste, so a teaspoon of dried valerian root powder is generally mixed into a cup of warm milk. A teaspoon of honey may also help to make the tea more palatable. Valerian is a powerful herb and should not be used in large amounts or over long periods of time unless on advice from a qualified herbal medicine practitioner.

- *Sweet basil and borage* — a good combination for increasing vitality if you're feeling weary.

- *Lavender* — an infusion of lavender leaves acts as a gentle sedative. Try this if you are anxious or having difficulty sleeping.

- *Peppermint* — another beneficial herb tea before bedtime, it is also beneficial for the relief of headaches and digestive problems.

- *St John's wort* — a tea made from the leaves of this herb will gently relax you and leave you feeling refreshed.

- *Thyme* — is an excellent tea to reduce tension and to relieve headaches.

- *Skullcap* — this bitter tea helps reduce stress, relieve headaches, promote sleep and act as a general tonic for the nervous system. Honey is often added to balance the bitter taste. While very effective, this herb should not be taken in large quantities.

Herbal preparations
are available commercially
in many forms,
from teabags to tinctures,
tablets to tonics.
They may contain a single herb
or a combination
that has been blended to treat
a particular condition.

Tinctures

Tinctures are created by steeping herbs, often for weeks, in pure or diluted alcohol. A small quantity of the tincture will then be further diluted and taken two or three times per day with meals. Most people choose to buy commercially prepared tinctures or else obtain them from a herbal medicine practitioner. In either case, the recommendations given for quantity and frequency of dose should be strictly observed.

• *Echinacea* — is a herb that assists the body's immune system in fighting infections. This is a suitable herb to take if you have been under stress for a long period of time, feel run down and seem to be more susceptible to minor infections, such as colds or blemished skin.

• *Marigold* — also known as calendula, this herb is beneficial in the treatment of anxiety and digestive complaints.

Inhalations

Inhalations are prepared by placing fresh herbs in a large bowl and pouring on near-boiling water. Place your face over the bowl with a towel over your head to form a tent, and breathe in the fragrant steam.

• *Sweet basil* — can calm nervousness and may be useful if you are not sleeping well.

• *Lavender* — makes a beautifully calming inhalation. Crush the fresh flowers before adding the water.

Compresses

To make a cold compress, take a clean cotton cloth and dip it into a cooled infusion or diluted tincture of your selected herbs. Wring the cloth and then place it directly onto the skin. It is time to replenish the cloth with the infusion when the cloth warms to body temperature.

• *Borage* — compresses made from the leaves of this herb are effective in reducing tiredness in the legs caused by too much standing.

• *Chamomile* — a compress of chamomile flowers will help relieve tired and strained eyes. For best results, lie on your back with the compress over your eyes and breathe deeply.

• *Rosemary* — whether an infusion of fresh rosemary leaves or the essential oil, rosemary provides effective relief from tension headaches. Place the compress across your brow and down onto your temples.

Massage

*O*ne of our instinctive reactions to pain or injury is to touch the area; we rub a sore joint and stroke the hand of someone in pain. Massage is an extension of this desire to touch and be touched, utilizing a range of different strokes and techniques.

Some of the benefits of receiving a massage are:
- Improved circulation
- More efficient digestion
- Faster elimination of waste products
- Relaxation of muscles and of the central nervous system
- Mental clarity
- General feeling of well-being
- Can be uplifting or deeply relaxing

While giving yourself a massage is not as luxurious as receiving a massage from someone else, it is an effective and enjoyable relaxation technique. One benefit of self-massage is that you can feel where you want to focus most attention and feel when one area has had enough massage. You may choose to undress for a self-massage if time and privacy permit and make use of a good massage oil such as avocado or sweet almond oil and a blend of essential oils (see page 20). If you choose not to undress, loosen or remove any tight-fitting clothing.

Preparation

Do your best to ensure you will be comfortable throughout the massage. The room should be pleasantly warm but not hot; dimmed lighting or candle light and some soft relaxing music help create a nurturing and peaceful atmosphere. If you are undressing for the massage have plenty of towels available to drape over the parts of your body you're not working on, otherwise you may feel the cold more as you relax. Try and ensure you won't be disturbed. Disconnect the telephone or turn on the answering machine; if there are others at home let them know you want some quiet time alone.

Two of the most important elements in a good self-massage are breathing and rhythm, so begin by making sure you are comfortable and take a few moments to focus on your breathing. Decide before you begin whether you want to relax deeply or energize yourself for the day ahead. If deep relaxation is your goal, use long, slow strokes; alternatively, if you want to feel vital and alert at the end of the massage use faster, shorter strokes.

Massage movements

- *Stroking* — long gentle strokes using both hands simultaneously or alternating
- *Effleurage* — long, even strokes using firm pressure in one direction and light pressure in the opposite direction (on arms and legs, firm pressure should always be used toward the heart). Keep contact with your body between the strokes.
- *Petrissage* — a rhythmic kneading movement with one hand holding and squeezing while the other hand releases. Particularly useful on the fleshy parts of the body.
- *Frictions* — small, circular movements made with the pads of the thumbs or fingers. Use this movement to work on areas that feel tight.
- *Tapotement* — brisk, rhythmic movements used on fleshy areas of the body to stimulate circulation. Do not use these movements around the kidney area, over the spine, behind the knees or on any area where there is little flesh between skin and bone. Includes:
  - *"Flicking"* — using the little finger side of your hands, palms facing each other, hands relaxed and alternately bouncing off the skin.
  - *"Plucking"* — pieces of flesh are picked up between thumb and fingers with alternate hands.
  - *"Cupping"* — hands and wrists are relaxed with fingers held closely together and arched to form a cup. Each hand alternately strikes the skin creating a hollow sound.
  - *"Pummelling"* — both hands are held in a loose fist. Using the little finger side, the fists are lightly bounced off the skin, alternating between hands.

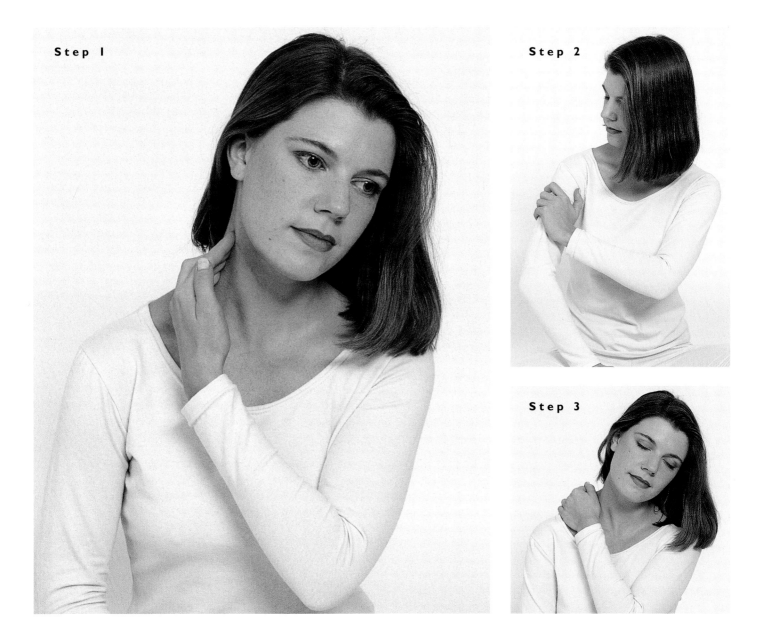

Step 1

Step 2

Step 3

Massage sequences

If you have time, work through each of these sequences one after the other. Alternatively, you can complete just one section as a mini-massage.

Neck, shoulders and arms

Sit on the floor, in a chair, or lie with your back on the floor, your knees bent and your feet flat on the floor.

1. Using your right hand, stroke from the bottom of your skull, down the left side of your neck to your shoulder, over your shoulder and down your arm to the elbow. Glide your hand gently back to the base of your skull and repeat two or three times.

2. With your right hand, use gentle kneading movements and work from your neck down to your wrist, gently glide your hand back to your neck and repeat.

3. Use circular friction movements to work more deeply into the muscles. Begin at the back of your neck, beside the spine and work out towards to the side of the neck, down to your shoulder. Glide hand to your wrist and work up your forearm to your elbow with circular frictions. Repeat.

4. Repeat steps 1 to 3 using your left hand on the right side of your body.

When you are massaging yourself, try to clear your mind and focus on the sensation alone. It is important to be comfortable and to keep all your muscles relaxed.

Step 3

Step 9

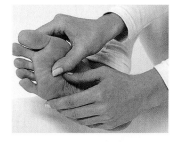

Step 6

Legs and feet

Sit on the floor with one leg extended in front of you and the other bent at the knee so you can hold your foot. Work on one entire leg first and then repeat the steps with your other leg.

1. Holding the top of your foot with one hand, use firm strokes along the sole of your foot from toes to ankle. Glide hand back to toes and repeat three or four times.

2. Gently roll each toe between your thumb and first finger and then give each toe a gentle pull.

3. Using both thumbs and firm pressure, work with small circular frictions from the ankle to the toes covering all of the sole.

4. Holding your foot with one hand, use a flicking motion over the sole.

5. Repeat step 1.

6. Bend the knee of the leg you have been working on and, starting from the instep, stroke both hands up the shin, over the knee and up the length of your thigh. Repeat this stroke two to three times.

7. With your knee still bent, draw both hands up from your ankle, and up the back of your leg. Repeat two to three times.

8. Using a kneading movement, work on the back of your leg, firstly around your calf muscle and then on the back of your thigh. Don't knead your knee, instead use small, light frictions around the kneecap.

9. Knead the top and sides of your thigh. Then use small circular frictions on any place that feels tight.

Step 1

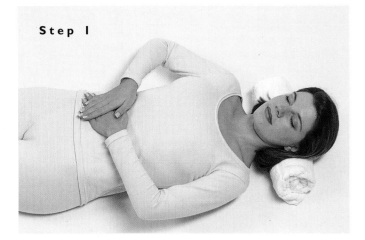

Step 3

Abdomen and chest

Lie on your back with a towel or pillow supporting your head, knees bent and feet flat on the floor.

1. With one hand over the other, stroke in a clockwise direction around your abdomen.

2. Using a gentle plucking movement with thumb and index fingers, lift the flesh of the abdominal area.

3. Next, hold your right hand flat against your lower abdomen, pull your hand up firmly toward the bottom of the rib cage, turn your hand so that your fingers point across your body and push across to the left hand side, then push down firmly with the heel of the hand from the rib cage to the lower abdomen. This movement assists the digestive process, which can become sluggish when we are stressed.

4. Move your hands to the center of your collarbone, gently stroke from the center out to the shoulders using your fingertips.

5. Follow this with gentle circular frictions around the chest and under the collarbone. Then repeat step 4.

Step 5

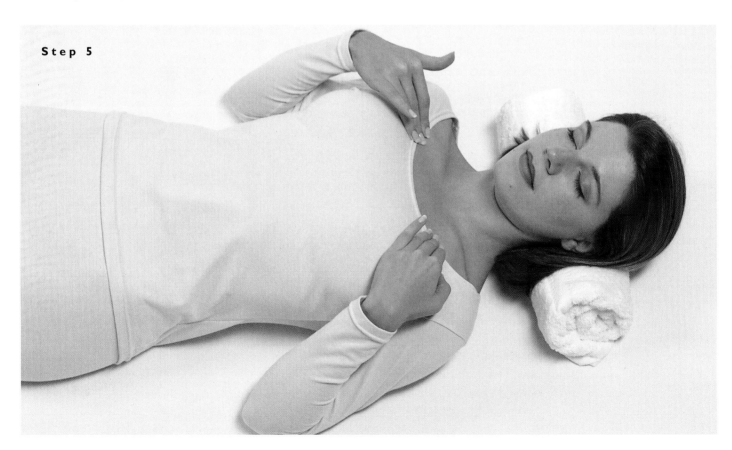

Step 1

Step 2

Face and scalp

A face and scalp massage alone can help relieve tension headaches, increase your energy levels and help improve your circulation, thus improving your appearance. It is worth using a very small amount of good quality light oil or a little moisturizer so you don't drag the skin of your face. It is also a good idea to ensure your fingernails are short and smooth to avoid injuring your skin or eyes during the massage. This routine can be carried out lying down or seated.

1. Place both hands at the base of your skull with your fingertips meeting in the middle. Using small circular frictions, gradually work your way to the sides of your head, just behind the ears. You may like to pay more attention to any spots that feel tender or tight.

2. Gradually work your way upwards, continuing with the frictions until your hands meet at the top of your head. Then massage the whole of your scalp in this way.

Step 3

3. Place both hands over your eyes with your fingers on your forehead and the heels of your hands on your cheeks. Spend a few moments like this breathing deeply.

4. Stroke along the sides of your nose, along your cheekbones to your ears. Run your fingertips down along the jaw line until your hands meet at your chin. Repeat two or three times.

5. Gently knead along the jaw line from your chin to your ears. Then gently knead your ears upwards from the lobes.

6. With very light, circular movements, massage all around the mouth, cheeks, the sides of the nose and the eyes. Stroke over the eyebrows and down around the top of your cheekbone with your middle finger until you reach the top of your nose, as pictured below.

7. Apply gentle pressure to the inside of the eye socket and hold for several seconds.

8. Using your fingertips, stroke upwards from the bridge of your nose to the top of your forehead. Repeat this several times.

9. Now massage with both hands, using small circular movements from the bridge of your nose to your hairline, then down to your temples.

10. Finish your massage with extremely light stroking all over your face and take a few deep breaths before gently proceeding with your day.

Step 4

Step 6

Meditation

No longer confined to the realm of mystics, meditation is widely recognized as one of the most effective tools for relaxation and overall health.

*M*editation can take you into a state where your body is completely relaxed and your mind is alert, yet still and peaceful. Many studies have been carried out on meditation and its effects on the physical body. Findings show that meditation reduces the body's metabolism, breath rate and heart rate. It can also reduce blood pressure and increase the speed with which the body eliminates chemicals, like blood lactate, produced when we are under stress. In short, meditation achieves the opposite effect on the body to the "fight or flight" response.

Other less tangible benefits associated with regular practice of meditation are clarity of mind, mental alertness, improved creativity, the ability to concentrate for longer periods of time, and improved co-ordination.

Like most things, meditation improves with practice. Start by meditating for just a few minutes, gradually increasing the length of time. If you begin by trying to meditate for half an hour or more, you are likely to become frustrated (which is counter to your motivation for doing it in the first place) and give up. Try and make a regular time each day for meditation and persevere. Some people find it most convenient to meditate in the morning when they are alert, while others find that meditation can encourage sound sleep. There are many different ways to meditate so experiment to find which one is most suitable for you.

Preparation

Find a quiet place that is free of distractions. Before you begin the meditation ensure you are comfortable — wear loose clothing and make sure you are warm. There are a variety of positions you can try, but whichever one you use, it is important that your spine remains straight.

Meditation positions

• Sitting on the ground cross-legged. You may like to support your back against a wall.
• Sitting in a straight-backed chair with hands lying loosely in your lap, palms facing upward.
• Lying on your back (if you feel you may fall asleep, try another position).
• Lotus or half-lotus position (if this is comfortable).
• Kneeling position with hands resting face up on the thighs. A meditation stool will make this more comfortable.

Focusing on the breath

Begin by taking very deep, smooth breaths. Be aware of how the air feels as you draw it through your nose, how your diaphragm feels as it contracts downward, the expansion of your rib cage, the sensation of the air being expelled through your mouth. As thoughts move into your mind, do not attempt to get rid of them. Instead, try to be an observer to your thoughts; don't judge them as right or wrong, silly or distracting, just allow them to come and go without becoming emotionally involved or allowing them to develop. Then consciously return your focus to your breath.

Using a mantra

A mantra is a word or phrase that is repeated, either audibly or silently, over and over again as a way of concentrating the mind. If you are meditating for relaxation choose a word or phrase that has a positive meaning for you and repeat this as you keep your breathing in a slow, even rhythm.

Focusing on an object

Light a candle or choose a small beautiful object like a single flower, a shell, or a piece of stone or crystal. Place this object at eye level, 1 to 2 feet (30 to 60 cms) away from you. Settle into your chosen position and begin to breathe deeply and evenly, focusing your attention on the object. As thoughts enter your mind, observe them objectively and without judgment, and bring your focus back to the object.

Guided meditations

If you have difficulty in meditating, you may like to try one of the many guided meditation audio cassettes available. These will lead you through a process that will assist you in focusing on your breath and on relaxing parts of your body. You may also like to make your own guide by reading onto a tape while you play soothing music in the background. Writing your own guided relaxation has the advantage of being in a language you respond to and understand, while proceeding at a comfortable pace for you. Begin with instructions to focus on your breath followed by instructions to relax all parts of your body, starting at your toes and working your way up to your scalp. Write your script down and read it a few times before making the recording; this helps you to speak slowly, smoothly and with clarity.

Music

People respond to music on a highly individual level. What one person may find relaxing and soothing, another may find boring or irritating. When we hear a piece of music we may recall the emotional experiences of other times we heard that music. There are, however, particular pieces of music that are likely to assist you in achieving a relaxed state.

When choosing music for relaxation, it is important to establish what you want to achieve. Do you want to reach a state of deep relaxation? Or do you wish to focus while you work or study? Perhaps you need a boost of energy.

Music whose tempo is faster than our resting heartbeat will often have the effect of increasing our heart rate, breathing and blood pressure. Similarly, music with a slower tempo can assist in lowering them.

Music performed at a slow, even tempo with wind (breath) instruments such as the clarinet and flute can be relaxing, as we may unconsciously slow our breathing to match that of the performer. Stringed instruments are common in music that is relaxing; this music also aids us in focusing our attention and maintaining mental clarity.

To relax deeply, music with a slow tempo and even rhythm are most effective. Much of the new music written for relaxation utilizes long sustained notes and may incorporate sounds from nature such as bird song.

Pieces for solo instruments, two instruments, or for small chamber groups help the mind focus. Most music of the Baroque period is useful for this purpose.

Energizing music will generally have a faster pace and may be more complex in its instrumentation.

When using music for relaxation, the volume should not be too high as loud sounds are stressful to the body.

You may like to incorporate music into other relaxation techniques such as meditation, visualization, self-massage or a bath. The following list provides an introduction to suitable music of the Baroque period (17th and first half of 18th centuries), Classical period (c.1750-c.1830) and Romantic period (19th century).

Focusing music
• Gregorian Chants (Abbey of Solesmes, France is recommended)

From the Baroque period
• *Goldberg Variations* by J.S. Bach (piano or harpsichord)
• *Well-Tempered Clavier* Books I and II by J.S. Bach (piano or harpsichord)
• Suites for cello solo by J.S. Bach, esp. No. 3 in C
• *Brandenburg Concertos* by J.S. Bach esp. No. 3 (strings)
• Sonatas for Viola da Gamba and Keyboard by J.S. Bach esp. 2nd movement BWV 1029,
• Sonatas for Violin and Keyboard by J.S. Bach
• Sonatas for harpsichord by Scarlatti
• *Water Music* by Handel (orchestral)
• Music for harpsichord by Handel
• Trio Sonata in D minor by Telemann
• Suite in A minor for Recorder and Strings by Telemann

From the Classical period
• Flute Concerto No. 1 in G Major by Mozart
• Piano concertos by Mozart
• String Quartet No. 14 in D minor D810 by Schubert ("Death and the Maiden")
• Piano Trio in E Flat D.897 by Schubert (Notturno Op. Posth. 148)

From the Romantic period

- Waltzes by Chopin (piano solo)
- *Songs Without Words* for piano by Mendelssohn (piano solo)
- String Quartet No. 12 in F, Op. 96 B179 by Dvorak ("American")
- *Scenes from Childhood* by Schumann (piano solo)
- *Songs of the Auvergne* (soprano and orchestra)

Energizing and uplifting

From the Baroque period

- *The Four Seasons* by Vivaldi (violin with stringed orchestra)
- Affettuoso from Trio Sonata in G major by Telemann
- Prelude to Sonata in B minor Op. 1 No. 11 by Vivaldi
- Chorus: (68) *Wir setzen uns mit Tranen nieder* from *St Matthew Passion* by J.S. Bach

From the Classical period

- Serenade K185, 2nd movement by Mozart
- Piano concertos by Mozart
- 3rd movement, Piano Sonata Op. 27 No. 2 by Beethoven ("Moonlight")
- 1st movement from Piano Sonata Op. 13 by Beethoven ("Pathetique")
- Piano Sonata Op. 57 by Beethoven ("Appassionata")
- Piano Sonata Op. 53 by Beethoven ("Walstein")
- Piano Sonata Op. 31 No. 2 by Beethoven ("Tempest")
- Symphony No. 9 by Beethoven ("Choral")
- Piano Concertos Nos 1, 3, 4, 5 by Beethoven
- Piano Trio in E Flat D.929 Op. 100 by Schubert (piano, violin, cello)

From the Romantic period

- Ballades by Chopin (piano solo)
- Polonaises by Chopin (piano solo)
- Piano Concerto No. 1 by Tchaikovsky
- *Rhapsody on a Theme of Paganini* by Rachmaninov (for piano and orchestra)
- Piano Concerto No. 2 by Rachmaninov

From the French Impressionists and early 20th century

- 1st and 3rd movements from *Sonatine* by Ravel (piano solo)
- Piano Concerto No. 3 by Prokofiev

Calming and soothing music

From the Baroque period

- Suite in A minor for Recorder and Strings by Telemann
- Canon in D by Pachelbel (violins and basso continuo)
- Adagio in G minor by Albinoni (strings and organ)
- Prelude No. 8 in E Flat minor from *The Well-tempered* Clavier Book I by J.S. Bach (piano or harpsichord)
- Concerto in G minor for Keyboard and Strings BWV 1068, 2nd movement by J.S. Bach

From the Classical period

- "Laudate Dominum" aria from *Vesperae solennes de confessore*, K339 by Mozart (soprano and orchestra)
- Slow movements from Piano Concertos Nos. 20, 21, 23, 24 by Mozart
- Clarinet Concerto in A, 2nd movement, by Mozart
- Piano Sonata Op. 27 No. 2, 1st movement, by Beethoven ("Moonlight")
- Piano Sonata Op. 13, 2nd movement, by Beethoven ("Pathetique)
- Symphony No. 7, slow movement, by Beethoven
- String Quartet in D minor, 2nd movement, by Schubert ("Death and the Maiden"),
- Piano Trio in E Flat D.929 Op.100, 2nd movement, by Schubert (piano, violin, cello)

From the Romantic period

- The complete Nocturnes by Chopin (piano solo)
- Romance and Larghetto from Piano Concerto No.1 in E minor Op. 11 by Chopin (piano and orchestra)
- *Andante Spinato* by Chopin (piano solo)
- *Romeo and Juliet Fantasy Overture* by Tchaikovsky (orchestral)
- Piano Quintet in A Op. 81 by Dvorak (piano and string quartet)
- Largo from Symphony No. 9 in E minor Op. 95 by Dvorak ("From The New World")
- "Song to the Moon" from *Russalka* by Dvorak (soprano and orchestra)
- *Vocalise* by Rachmaninov (soprano and orchestra)
- "Ave Maria" and "Oh Divine Redeemer" by Gounod (soprano and piano)

From the French Impressionists and early 20th century

- *La Mer* by Debussy (orchestral)
- *Daphnis et Chloe* Suite No. 2 by Debussy (orchestral)
- *Deux Arabesques* Nos. 1 & 2 by Debussy (piano solo)
- "Clair de Lune" from *Suite bergamasque* by Debussy (piano solo)
- "The Snow is Dancing" from *Children's Corner* by Debussy (piano solo)
- *Images* by Debussy (piano solo)
- *L'isle Joyeuse* by Debussy (piano solo)
- *Sonatine*, 2nd movement, by Ravel (piano solo)
- *Pavane for a Dead Princess* by Ravel (orchestral or piano version)
- Arrangements for flute and harp of pieces by Debussy, Ravel, Faure and others
- *Fantasia on a Theme of Thomas Tallis* by Vaughan Williams (orchestral)
- *The Lark Ascending* by Vaughan Williams (orchestral)

Reflexology

The feet and hands are often neglected, yet it is surprising how comforting massaging these areas can be — and how much benefit this can bring to the rest of your body.

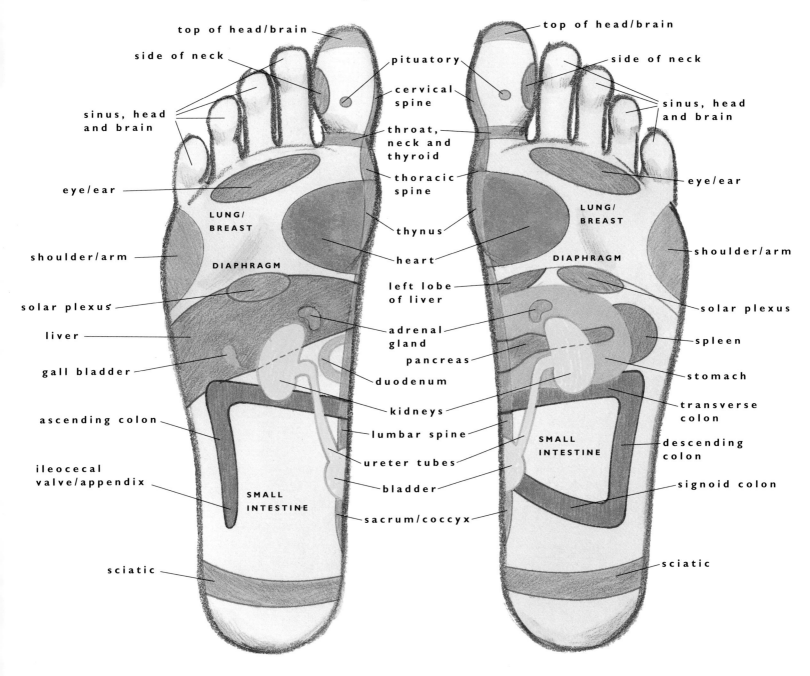

top of head/brain

side of neck

sinus, head and brain

eye/ear

shoulder/arm

solar plexus

liver

gall bladder

ascending colon

ileocecal valve/appendix

sciatic

LUNG/BREAST

DIAPHRAGM

SMALL INTESTINE

pituatory

cervical spine

throat, neck and thyroid

thoracic spine

thynus

heart

left lobe of liver

adrenal gland

pancreas

duodenum

kidneys

lumbar spine

ureter tubes

bladder

sacrum/coccyx

top of head/brain

side of neck

sinus, head and brain

eye/ear

shoulder/arm

solar plexus

spleen

stomach

transverse colon

descending colon

signoid colon

sciatic

LUNG/BREAST

DIAPHRAGM

SMALL INTESTINE

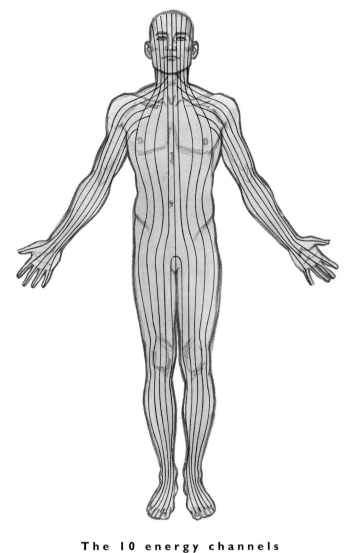

**T h e 1 0 e n e r g y c h a n n e l s
k n o w n a s z o n e s**

*T*he origins of reflexology can be traced back to ancient Chinese and Egyptian times. In the West, it was developed as a healing art in the early 1900s by an American, Dr William Fitzgerald. Dr Fitzgerald determined that parts of the body related to and affected other parts and that this principle could be used to relieve pain.

Reflexology is based on the concept that a system of ten energy channels runs vertically through the body ending at the feet. The feet are a microcosm of the whole body and working on particular places on the feet can therefore stimulate or balance other parts of the body.

Reflexology has been shown to be very effective as a relaxation technique and can relieve pain as well as stress and tension.

It is easy to learn some of the basic techniques yourself and reflexology can be part of a daily routine; however it should be remembered that reflexology is seen as a means to help the body heal itself, not as a cure for any particular problem. It is important to realize that a tender part on the foot does not necessarily mean there is something wrong with the corresponding organ or part of the body. Attempting to use a superficial knowledge of reflexology to diagnose is likely to cause a lot of anxiety and is very unlikely to be accurate.

If you massage your own feet you may feel small crystals beneath the service of the skin. It is believed that these are sediment deposits that settle in the body and that regular reflexology treatment will break them up for reabsorption into the body and then elimination — returning your body to balance.

Reflexology is difficult to practice on yourself, but if you can find another person interested in relaxation you can swap reflexology sessions. A treatment from a qualified reflexologist is a worthwhile experience just to see how relaxed the rest of your body can feel by working on the feet alone.

Always work with clean feet and clean hands and make sure the nails of both are short and smooth to avoid scratching the other person. Your partner should be seated or lying down. Shoes and socks should be removed, and you may wish to apply talcum powder to the feet.

Begin the session by holding your hands lengthwise against your partner's feet and then firmly and smoothly stroking the sole of the foot. This may help to relieve any initial tension that can cause a ticklish response. Complete the movements you are going to use on one foot first and then on the other.

Introduce yourself to reflexology with the following routine, but as your confidence grows, experiment with other movements. Make sure your partner is comfortable, that their legs are supported throughout the session and that they realize they must tell you if a particular movement is painful or too tender to touch.

*The 10-step sequence illustrated here
provides a good introduction to the healing art of reflexology and
can be followed comfortably and safely at home.*

Step 1

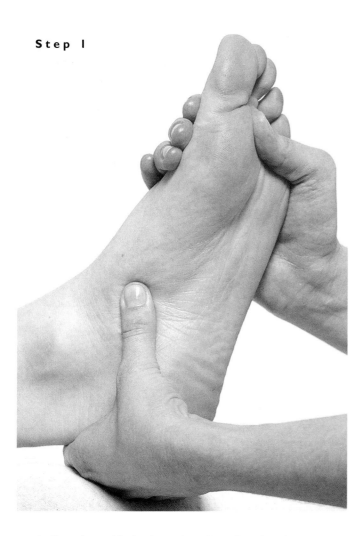

Step 2

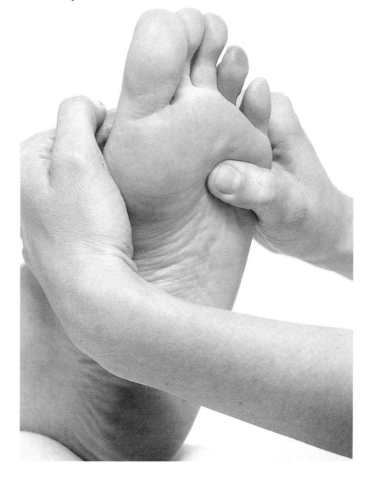

1. Cup the ankle in the palm of one hand and, supporting the instep of the foot with the other hand, very slowly and gently rotate the foot around the ankle, first one way and then the other. Only move the foot to the first sign of resistance. Then slowly and gently, flex and stretch the foot.

2. Next, place your hand around the top of the foot and gently squeeze the base of the big toe toward the base of the little toe — the hollow that results is the first point to use in this session. Release the toes and, using the pad of your thumb, press on this point for a few moments, then begin to make small circles on the point.

3. Hold the foot with both hands, your palms on the instep side of the foot. Gently move your hands in opposite directions to "wring" the foot. Move your hands up and down and repeat this movement so that you cover the entire foot.

Step 4

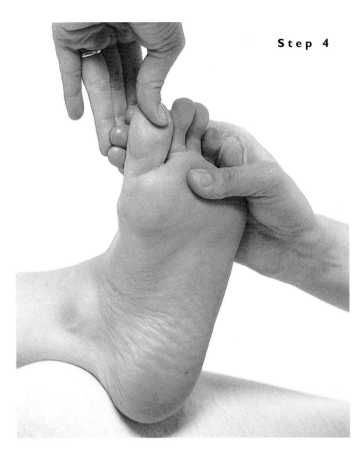

4. Hold the foot firmly and with the thumb and index finger of your other hand massage the whole of the big toe. Then gently rotate the toe, first one way and then the other, and finish by gently stretching the toe. Repeat this step for each toe. The toes correspond to the head and neck, so this is a particularly good area to work if the person is prone to tension headaches and muscular tension around the neck area.

5. Now make a fist with one hand and use this to support the foot. Using a gentle pressure with the other hand, work from the base of each toe down between the tendons of the foot. Continue until about half way down the foot.

6. Move one hand to cradle the ankle and, with the other hand still in a fist, use the flat surface created by the back of the fingers to slide from the top of the foot to the ankle. Repeat this two or three times with a firm pressure.

7. Hold the instep of the foot to support it and then, using the side of your thumb with short strokes, "walk" your thumb over the ball of the foot. The ball of the foot represents the lungs and chest area.

8. Keeping your supporting hand around the instep, use the other hand to work small circular movements all around the ankle and Achilles tendon. Work this area gently as it can be quite tender on a stressed person.

9. Now, using the pad of your thumb, move with firm circles over the edge and pad of the heel. This area corresponds to your lower back.

10. Finish the session by stroking the foot with the flat of your hand, from ankle to toes and then from the instep to the toes.

Step 5

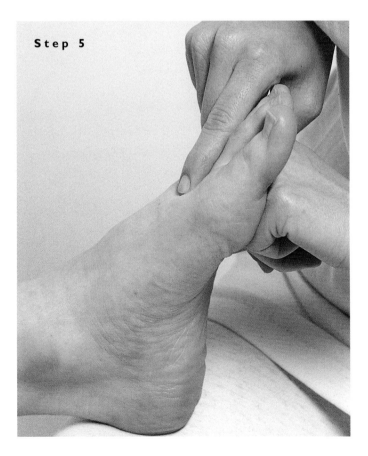

Step 7   Step 8

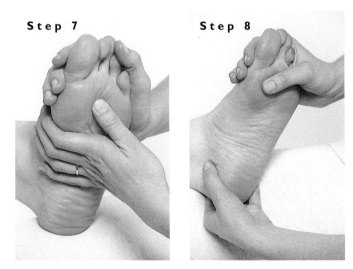

Yoga

*Yoga brings harmony
to our existence and nurtures
our whole being.
It is a gentle art involving
no strain or great exertion,
and can be practiced by anyone,
irrespective of age or
state of health*

The word "yoga" translates as "union", and the goal of those making yoga their way of life is to unite the mind, body and spirit. Its benefits are clarity of mind, increased powers of concentration, spiritual awareness, the ability to deeply relax, physical strength and flexibility. Originally from India, yoga is a complex and complete philosophy of life that has developed over thousands of years. It is not necessary, however, to dedicate your life to the practice of yoga to effectively use it as a relaxation technique. The following "asanas" or exercises can provide a gentle exercise routine and provide a means for releasing stress and tension. All exercises should be carried out slowly and while observing the suggested breathing.

Step 1 & 13

Salute to the sun (Surya Namaskar)

The salute to the sun is a sequence of exercises that was traditionally practiced at sunrise each morning.

1. Stand straight with legs and feet together, palms touching in a "prayer" position.

2. Inhale and raise both hands above your head, bend slightly backward from the waist and tilt head back.

Step 3

3. Exhale and slowly bring your upper body forward and down. Place hands flat on the floor either side of your feet. (bend knees if necessary.)

4. Inhale, moving your right foot backward and lower your right knee to the floor. Look upward and arch back slightly, keeping hips as low as possible.

5. Exhale and move the left foot back to join the right, taking the weight of your body on hands and toes. Back and arms should be straight.

6. Inhale as you slowly lower your knees. Keeping your toes curled, move your buttocks back toward your heels.

Step 2

Step 4

Step 6

Step 7

Step 8

Step 9

Step 10

Step 11

7. Exhale and move your chest along the floor, keeping hips and buttocks up.

8. Inhale and lower your hips to the ground, legs together with the soles of your feet pointing upward, your back arched, shoulders relaxed and head facing up and back.

9. Exhale as you curl your toes under and move your buttocks toward the ceiling creating an inverted "V" shape. Heels should be on the floor, head should be dropped forward.

10. Inhale and move your left foot backward and drop the left knee as in step 4.

11. Exhale and bring your left foot forward as you bend at the waist as in step 3.

12. Inhale and take both arms above your head as in step 2.

13. Exhale as you lower your arms, bringing your palms together as in step 1.

This sequence of exercise may be repeated alternating which leg is used first in steps 4 and 10. Take a few deep breaths in still position before continuing.

Step 12

Step 2

Step 3

The cat

This exercise is especially useful for relaxing muscles in your back, neck and buttocks and if practiced regularly helps to increase the muscle tone and suppleness of these areas.

1. Position yourself on your hands and knees with arms straight and legs shoulder-width apart.

2. Exhale as you tuck your buttocks and head in, and arch your back toward the ceiling.

3. Inhale as you bring your buttocks and head up and curve your back toward the floor.

4. Repeat steps 2 and 3 four or five times.

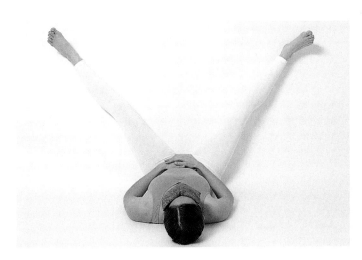

Wall stand

This position is useful in the relief of tension headaches and also helps reduce fatigue in the legs. Firstly, sit on the floor, one hip against a wall. Slowly swing your legs around, one at a time, so they are pointing up, resting against the wall. As part of the same movement, pivot your trunk around and lie down on the floor (use a rolled towel to support your head if necessary). Make sure that your buttocks are against the wall, that your upper body is flat and at right angles with your legs, which should be straight. Relax your arms and feet and hold this position for about 5 minutes (see right). As an alternative position, you may like to spread your legs apart and feel the different muscles this uses (see above).

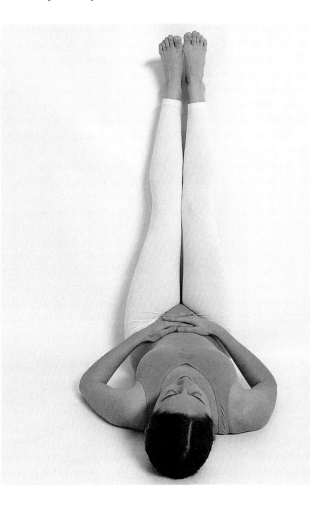

Yoga mudra

This exercise helps release tension in the back and shoulder areas and works to expand the chest encouraging deep, relaxing breathing.

Step 1

1. Sit in a kneeling position with your back straight and your buttocks resting on your heels.

2. Inhale as you bring both arms in front of your body, circle your arms to the back and clasp hands and exhale.

3. Inhale and pull shoulders back.

4. Exhale and stretch your body forward from the hips, placing your head on the floor.

Step 5

5. Inhale. As you exhale, lift your clasped hands up toward the ceiling.

6. Inhale as you slowly lower your arms, unclasp your hands and allow them to rest at your sides.

7. Breath deeply for a few moments in this position and then, as you inhale raise your body slowly back into the seated position from which you began (see opposite). Repeat two or three times.

Step 4

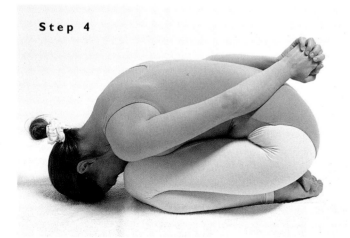

Step 6

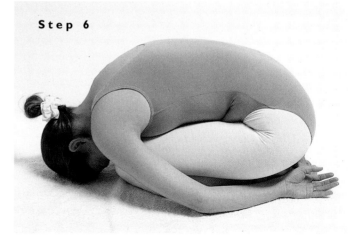

Step 7

Index

About the author

Fiona Toy has had an interest in natural therapies from the age of 16,
and holds a Diploma in Remedial Massage. She has also had her share of stressful jobs,
from a busy cafe/catering businesss to management positions, and knows the challenge
of dealing with stress and discovering relaxation techniques
that fit into individual, changing lifestyles. Fiona now edits and publishes
Directions: The Directory of Holistic Health and Creative Living.

Acknowledgments

The publishers wish to thank Karen Bailey and Amalia Matheson
for their assistance.
For photograph (page 6-7): "Une Chaumiere et un Coeur" from
Fine Art Photographic Library, London and Galerie Berko Belgium
Page 50: "Solo", Charles A. Buchel, International Photographic Library

First published in Great Britain in 1996
by Chancellor Press
a division of Reed Consumer Books
Michelin House, 81 Fulham Rd, London SW3 6RB

Published in conjunction with Lansdowne Publishing Pty Ltd
Level 5, 70 George Street, Sydney, NSW 2000, Australia

© Copyright: Lansdowne Publishing Pty Ltd
ISBN 1-85152-917-9
Set in Caslon 540 Roman on Quark Xpress
Printed in Singapore by Tien Wah Press (Pte) Ltd